STARS® D

York

Strategies **T**o **A**chieve **R**eading **S**uccess

ACKNOWLEDGMENTS

Product Development

Developers and Authors: Deborah Adcock, Joan Krensky

Contributing Writers: Patricia Delanie, Laura Johnson, Barbara Fierman

Editorial Project Managers

Deborah Adcock, Pamela Seastrand

Design

Cover Designer: Matt Pollock

Book Designer: Pat Lucas

Illustration/Photography Credits

©JupiterImages Corporation/pages 6, 7, 17, 22, 40, 55, 60, 81, 88, 96, 104, 110, 115, 138, 146

LuAnn Smith/pages 8, 11, 16, 27, 30, 33, 61, 62, 68, 70, 84, 86, 94, 119, 120

Jim Roldan/pages 12, 18, 23, 26, 47, 67, 74, 76, 123, 124, 130, 133, 136, 149

Susan Hawk/pages 36, 95, 140

Pat Lucas/page 42

Library of Winchester House, San Jose, CA/page 45

NASA/page 79

Roberto Castillo/Shutterstock.com/page 96

National Archives and Records Administration/page 98

Courtesy of Johnson Space Center/page 101

Gary Torrisi/page 108

Courtesy of Federation Internationale de Football Association, Zurich, Switzerland/page 123

Lisa Greenleaf/page 129

Vladislav Gurfinkel/Shutterstock.com/page 143

TABLE OF CONTENTS

PART ONE: Think About the Strategy

What Is Main Idea?

Books and stories all have a main idea. A movie or television show also has a main idea. The main idea tells what something is mostly about.

1 Write the name of a book you have read in school or at home.

_____

2 Write some of the things that happen in the book.

_____

_____

_____

_____

3 Tell what the book is mostly about.

_____

_____

_____

_____

Work with a Partner

- Tell your partner about a movie you have seen or a TV show you have watched.
- Then take turns telling about the main idea of the movie or TV show. Try to tell your main idea in one sentence.

- Identify a main idea in informational texts (**GPI.R.1**)
- Evaluate information, ideas, opinions, and themes in texts by identifying a central idea (**GPI.R.3**)
- Collect and interpret ideas from unfamiliar texts (**GPI.R.1**)
- Identify a conclusion that summarizes the main idea (**GPI.R.1**)
- Use evidence from stories to identify themes, actions, motivations (**GPI.R.2**)

4

How Do You Find the Main Idea?

You can find the main idea of most reading passages in the first or last sentence of the passage.

Read this passage about gravity. Think about the most important idea in the passage.

> The space environment is different from Earth's. There is no gravity in space. Gravity is what keeps us on the ground. In space, everything floats around.

1. Let's look at the chart below.

   The sentences in the top three boxes tell about the main idea of the passage, but they do not tell the most important idea.

2. Look again at the passage.
   The first sentence in the passage does tell the most important idea.
   This sentence tells what the passage is mostly about.

3. Write this main idea in the empty box below.

There is no gravity in space.	Gravity is what keeps us on the ground.	In space, everything floats around.

WHAT TO KNOW

The most important idea in a paragraph is called the **main idea**. The main idea tells what a paragraph is mostly about.

- The main idea is sometimes found in the first sentence of a paragraph.

- The main idea is sometimes found in the last sentence of a paragraph.

- The main idea is sometimes not found in any one sentence. You can figure out the main idea by asking yourself, "What is the most important idea in the paragraph?"

Read this paragraph about wolves. As you read, think about the most important idea in the paragraph.

Howling Wolves

Wolves howl as a way to talk with one another. Wolves howl to stay in touch with their pack before, during, and after a hunt. And they howl to warn other wolf packs to keep out of their territory. Sometimes, wolves howl just for fun. When many wolves are howling at the same time, each wolf howls a different note. Heard together, the wolves sound like a group of singers.

The first sentence of the paragraph states the most important idea:

Wolves howl as a way to talk with one another.

Read this paragraph about an unusual bicycle. As you read, think about the main idea of the paragraph. Then answer the questions.

An Extraordinary Bike

Bicycles have been around for more than 200 years. The first bikes weren't much fun to ride. Riders had to use their feet to push themselves along the ground. Then in the 1870s, a bike called the ordinary appeared. The ordinary was different from the early bikes. It had pedals, handlebars, and brakes. It also had a huge front wheel and a tiny back wheel. Each full turn of the big wheel made the bike go farther. The seat was almost on top of the front wheel. So getting on and off the ordinary was difficult. The rider also needed a lot of skill just to stay upright. Still, people enjoyed riding the ordinary. The ordinary was the first popular bike.

1. What is the main idea of the paragraph?
   - Ⓐ The ordinary had a huge front wheel.
   - Ⓑ Getting on and off the ordinary was difficult.
   - Ⓒ The ordinary was the first popular bike.
   - Ⓓ Riders used their feet to push the first bikes along.

2. Where or how did you find the main idea?
   - Ⓐ in the first sentence of the paragraph
   - Ⓑ in the last sentence of the paragraph
   - Ⓒ in the middle of the paragraph
   - Ⓓ by thinking about the most important idea in the paragraph

Work with a Partner

- Talk about your answers to the questions.
- Tell why you chose your answers.
- Then talk about what you have learned so far about finding main idea.

REVIEW

The main idea tells what a paragraph is mostly about.

- Read the first sentence of the paragraph. The main idea is sometimes found here.

- Read the last sentence of the paragraph. The main idea is sometimes found here.

- Sometimes, the main idea is not found in a sentence from the paragraph. You can figure out the main idea by thinking about the most important idea in the paragraph.

Read this story about skateboarding. As you read, ask yourself, "What is the story mostly about?" Then answer the questions.

Surfing on Land

Sal was a surfer. He lived in California during the 1950s. Some days, the ocean waves weren't big enough for Sal to ride his surfboard on. Sal and his surfer friends had nothing to do. They got bored. One day, Sal and the other surfers had an idea. They began nailing wheels from roller skates to narrow boards. They used these "skateboards" to "surf" on the street. Soon, skateboards were as popular as surfboards. But when people went skateboarding, no one ever got wet!

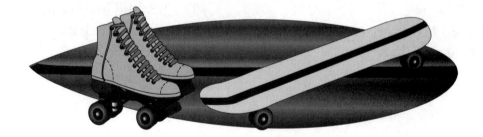

3. What is the story mostly about?
   - Ⓐ Sal and his friends got bored easily.
   - Ⓑ Surfers invented skateboarding in the 1950s.
   - Ⓒ Sal was a surfer in California during the 1950s.
   - Ⓓ Small waves are hard to surf.

4. Where or how did you find the main idea?
   - Ⓐ in the first sentence of the paragraph
   - Ⓑ in the last sentence of the paragraph
   - Ⓒ in the middle of the paragraph
   - Ⓓ by thinking about the most important idea in the paragraph

Which Answer Is Correct and Why?

Look at the answer choices for each question.
Read why each answer choice is correct or not correct.

3. **What is the story mostly about?**

   Ⓐ **Sal and his friends got bored easily.**

   This answer is not correct because the only reason that Sal and his friends were bored was that the waves were too small to ride.

   ● **Surfers invented skateboarding in the 1950s.**

   This answer is correct because it tells what all the sentences in the story are mostly about. It is the most important idea.

   Ⓒ **Sal was a surfer in California during the 1950s.**

   This answer is not correct because it is one idea in the story, but it is not the most important idea.

   Ⓓ **Small waves are hard to surf.**

   This answer is not correct because, even though it is true that small waves are hard to ride, this idea is not what the story is mostly about.

4. **Where or how did you find the main idea?**

   Ⓐ **in the first sentence of the paragraph**

   This answer is not correct because the first sentence is *"Sal was a surfer."* This is not the most important idea in the paragraph.

   Ⓑ **in the last sentence of the paragraph**

   This answer is not correct because the last sentence is *"But when people went skateboarding, no one ever got wet!"* This is not the most important idea in the paragraph.

   Ⓒ **in the middle of the paragraph**

   This answer is not correct because the middle of the paragraph tells about how skateboards were made and used. Also, the main idea is more often found in the first or last sentence of a paragraph, not in the middle of a paragraph.

   ● **by thinking about the most important idea in the paragraph**

   This answer is correct because the main idea is not found in the first sentence, the last sentence, or in the middle of the paragraph. The main idea is found by thinking about what all the sentences in the paragraph are mostly about.

MORE TO KNOW	• Each paragraph in a reading passage has one main idea. All the paragraphs together in a reading passage also have one main idea. The main idea of a reading passage is often found in the first or last paragraph. • The title of a reading passage tells something about the main idea.

Read this report about a girl's camp experience. Then answer the questions.

When I Grow Up

I plan to become an astronaut when I grow up. This has been my dream ever since I read about Sally Ride. She was the first American woman to travel in space.

This summer, I got the chance to experience what it's like to be an astronaut. I spent part of my vacation at a space camp for kids.

For six days, I got to do what an astronaut does. Part of my training included a "space mission." I worked with a team of other kids from all over the world. We took turns playing the roles of mission-control operators and shuttle-crew members. I discovered what it feels like to be weightless and to spin in orbit. I also learned how difficult it is to do anything while wearing a space suit!

5. What is the main idea of the first paragraph?
   Ⓐ More women are becoming astronauts.
   Ⓑ A girl plans to become an astronaut.
   Ⓒ Sally Ride is a heroine to girls.
   Ⓓ Sally Ride was the first woman in space.

6. What is the main idea of the last paragraph?
   Ⓐ Kids from all over the world trained together.
   Ⓑ The girl got to spin in orbit.
   Ⓒ The girl discovered what it's like to be weightless.
   Ⓓ For six days, the girl did what an astronaut does.

7. What is the report mostly about?
   Ⓐ training for a space mission
   Ⓑ the first American woman to travel in space
   Ⓒ a girl who wants to become an astronaut
   Ⓓ children who attended a space camp

8. Which of these is another good title for the report?
   Ⓐ "High Hopes for the Future"
   Ⓑ "The First Woman in Space"
   Ⓒ "Great Camps for Kids"
   Ⓓ "Mission Control"

Read this fable from Aesop. Then answer the questions.

A farmer's daughter had been out to milk the cows. She was returning to the dairy, carrying her pail of milk upon her head. As the milkmaid walked along, she began daydreaming.

"The milk in this pail will provide me with cream. I will make the cream into butter and take it to market to sell. With the money I make, I will buy a number of eggs. The eggs will hatch and produce a number of chickens. I shall sell some of my fowls, and with the money they will bring in, I will buy myself a new gown. I shall wear the gown when I go to the fair. All the young fellows will try to win my affection. But I shall toss my head and have nothing to say to them."

Forgetting all about the pail, the milkmaid acted out her last words and tossed her head. Down went the pail. All of the milk was spilled, and all of her dreams vanished in the air.

9. What is the main idea of paragraph 2?
   Ⓐ The cream from milk can be made into butter.
   Ⓑ The milkmaid would rather raise chickens than milk cows.
   Ⓒ The milkmaid dreams of all the things her milk will bring to her.
   Ⓓ The milkmaid likes fancy clothes.

10. The last paragraph is mostly about
   Ⓐ how the milkmaid's forgetfulness made her plans disappear.
   Ⓑ how the milkmaid acted selfishly.
   Ⓒ how mistakes happen to everyone.
   Ⓓ how the milkmaid worried that her father would be upset.

11. What is the fable mostly about?
   Ⓐ milk that vanishes into the air
   Ⓑ a girl who makes plans about things that haven't happened yet
   Ⓒ a daughter who behaves badly because she is greedy
   Ⓓ a milkmaid who wastes food

12. What is the best title for the fable?
   Ⓐ "Don't Cry over Spilled Milk"
   Ⓑ "The Farmer's Proud Daughter"
   Ⓒ "Don't Count Your Chickens Before They've Hatched"
   Ⓓ "Going to the Market"

TEST TIPS

- A test question about the main idea may ask you what a reading passage is *mostly* or *mainly* about.
- A test question about the main idea may ask you to choose the best title for a reading passage. A good title tells something about the main idea of the whole reading passage.

Read this story about a spider named Legs. Then answer questions about the story. Choose the best answer for Numbers 13 and 14.

Legs was a trap-door spider. He lived in a hole in the ground. The opening to his underground tunnel was a door made of dirt and silk. This trapdoor fit tightly over the opening, like a cork in a bottle. Every night, Legs lifted up the door and waited for his dinner. When an insect came near, Legs ran out and grabbed it.

Legs was mostly content, but one thing made him unhappy. He was tired of people always praising the work of web-building spiders. Legs wished more people knew that some spiders didn't build webs. Some spiders, like him, were brave hunters. After all, Legs didn't wait for food to enter his trap. He used his sharp eyes and fast legs to go after his meals. Legs hoped that someday his wish would come true, and he would get the attention he deserved.

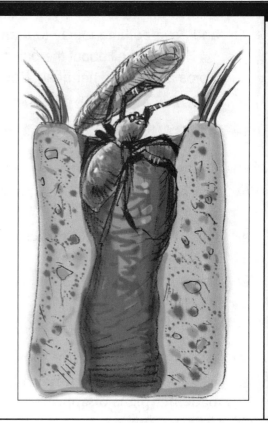

13. The story is mostly about
Ⓐ a spider who feels left out.
Ⓑ a proud web builder.
Ⓒ a spider who is never happy.
Ⓓ a trapdoor.

14. What is the best title for the story?
Ⓐ "Entering a Trap"
Ⓑ "One Wish"
Ⓒ "Through a Trapdoor"
Ⓓ "The Content Spider"

Read this article about paper money. Then answer questions about the article. Choose the best answer for Numbers 15 and 16.

There are seven paper bills used for money in the United States. These bills have values of $1, $2, $5, $10, $20, $50, and $100. On the front of each bill is the portrait of a great American. The faces of past presidents are printed on the $1, $2, $5, $20, and $50 bills. In order, these presidents are George Washington, Thomas Jefferson, Abraham Lincoln, Andrew Jackson, and Ulysses S. Grant.

Alexander Hamilton's face appears on the $10 bill. Benjamin Franklin's face appears on the $100 bill. Hamilton was the first Secretary of the Treasury. Franklin was a printer, an inventor, and a patriot.

Years ago, bills were printed with much higher values—$500, $1,000, $5,000, and even $10,000. These bills were not very popular, however. The government stopped printing them in 1969.

15. The article is mostly about
   Ⓐ famous Americans.
   Ⓑ the people whose faces appear on paper bills.
   Ⓒ past presidents of the United States.
   Ⓓ paper bills with high values that are no longer printed.

16. Which of these is the best title for the article?
   Ⓐ "A New Look for Paper Money"
   Ⓑ "Great Presidents"
   Ⓒ "Getting Your Face Known"
   Ⓓ "Portraits on Bills"

What Are Facts and Details?

Everything you read has facts and details. Shows you watch on TV or movies you see at the theater also have facts and details. Facts and details tell more about the main idea.

1 Write the main idea of a TV show you watched in the past few days.

_____

_____

_____

2 Write three important things that happened in the TV show. Each one should tell more about the main idea.

_____

_____

_____

_____

_____

Work with a Partner

- Tell your partner about a story you read or your favorite movie.
- Take turns telling about the main character in the story or movie. Tell all the facts and details that describe this character.
- When you are done, choose one word to describe the character.

- Identify supporting details in informational texts (**GPI.R.1**)
- Evaluate content by identifying important and unimportant details (**GPI.R.3**)
- Evaluate information, ideas, opinions, and themes in texts by identifying supporting details (**GPI.R.3**)
- Collect and interpret data and facts (**GPI.R.1**)
- Use evidence from stories to identify themes, actions, motivations (**GPI.R.2**)

How Do You Find Facts and Details?

You can find the facts and details in a reading passage by thinking about the main idea. Once you know the main idea, you can find the details that tell more about the main idea.

Read this passage about a rabbit. Think about what the passage is mostly about.

> There was once a nervous rabbit sleeping under a palm tree. A coconut fell from the tree and startled her. She ran into the jungle to warn her friends. <u>The panicked rabbit thought the sky was breaking apart.</u>

1. First, let's find the main idea of the passage. The main idea is found in the last sentence. It is underlined for you.

2. Next, find the details that tell more about the main idea.

   Look at the chart below. The box at the top tells the main idea.

   The boxes along the bottom tell more about the main idea. They show the facts and details that help explain the main idea.

3. Fill in the detail that is missing from the last box below.

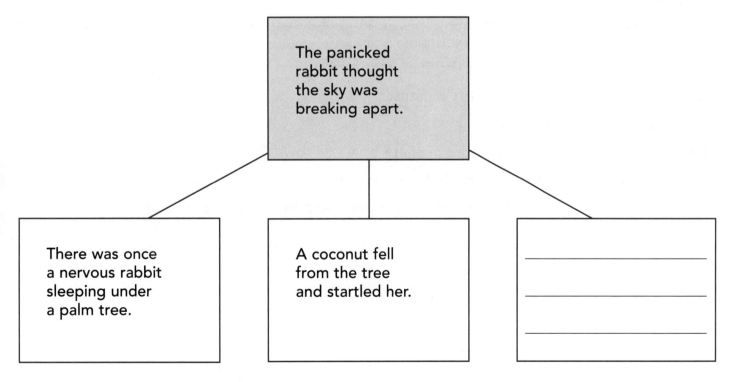

WHAT TO KNOW

Sentences that tell more about the main idea are called **facts and details**. Facts and details explain or support the most important idea in the paragraph.

- Facts and details provide information about the main idea.
- Facts and details often tell about the *who, what, where, when, why,* and *how* of the main idea.

Read this paragraph about animal names. The main idea is found in the first sentence. It is underlined for you. As you read, think about the sentences that tell more about the main idea.

What's in a Name?

Different terms are used to name male and female animals. On a farm, the chickens are roosters or hens. The horses are stallions or mares. The sheep are rams or ewes, and the pigs are boars or sows. In the woods, the deer and rabbits are bucks or does. Male elephants, whales, moose, and cattle are bulls, and the females are cows.

The sentences that tell more about the main idea are:

On a farm, the chickens are roosters or hens.

The horses are stallions or mares.

The sheep are rams or ewes, and the pigs are boars or sows.

In the woods, the deer and rabbits are bucks or does.

Male elephants, whales, moose, and cattle are bulls, and the females are cows.

Read this paragraph about Michael. The main idea is found in the last sentence. It is underlined for you. As you read, think about the facts and details that tell more about the main idea. Then answer the questions.

How Lucky Do You Feel?

Michael believes that doing certain things will bring him good luck. He always carries a rabbit's foot. He looks on the ground for pennies that are heads up. Sometimes, he even wears his clothes inside out. Michael also thinks that avoiding certain things can prevent bad luck. He won't walk under a ladder or open an umbrella indoors. And he'd never let a black cat cross his path. Michael's friends laugh at his strange beliefs, but he doesn't care. <u>Michael's superstitions make him feel safe.</u>

1. What is something that Michael believes will bring him good luck?

    Ⓐ walking under a ladder

    Ⓑ finding a penny heads up

    Ⓒ laughing a lot

    Ⓓ opening an umbrella indoors

2. Which detail tells why Michael always carries a rabbit's foot?

    Ⓐ He believes that doing certain things will bring him good luck.

    Ⓑ Sometimes, he even wears his clothes inside out.

    Ⓒ He won't walk under a ladder or open an umbrella indoors.

    Ⓓ His friends laugh at his strange beliefs, but he doesn't care.

Work with a Partner

- Talk about your answers to the questions.
- Tell why you chose your answers.
- Then talk about what you have learned so far about recalling facts and details.

REVIEW	Facts and details explain or support the main idea.
	• Look for sentences that provide information about the main idea.
	• Look for sentences that tell about the *who, what, where, when, why,* and *how* of the main idea.

Read this article about a fun sport. As you read, ask yourself, "What is the main idea? What facts and details tell *more* about the main idea?" Then answer the questions.

A Unique Game of Catch

Many people enjoy playing a game of Frisbee®. A Frisbee doesn't cost much, and the game can be played almost anywhere outdoors.

Some students at Yale University invented this sport. The first Frisbee was a metal pie pan. Its original spelling was *frisbie*. It was named after the Frisbie Bakery in Bridgeport, Connecticut. Yale students often bought pies at a nearby bakery. After eating the pies, they liked to toss the empty pie pans back and forth.

The metal frisbies, of course, were not safe. Anyone hit by the flying disk could get a bad lump or wound. So, in 1957, Walter Morrison and the Wham-O Manufacturing Company began making plastic models. The toy's name was changed to Frisbee, which is what it's still called today.

3. Who first had the idea of playing Frisbee?
   Ⓐ a baker in Bridgeport, Connecticut
   Ⓑ some students at Frisbie High School
   Ⓒ some students at Yale University
   Ⓓ Walter Morrison

4. Where were the first plastic Frisbees made?
   Ⓐ at Yale University
   Ⓑ at the Wham-O Manufacturing Company
   Ⓒ at the Frisbie Bakery
   Ⓓ at the Walter Morrison Manufacturing Company

Which Answer Is Correct and Why?

Look at the answer choices for each question.
Read why each answer choice is correct or not correct.

3. Who first had the idea of playing Frisbee?

   Ⓐ a baker in Bridgeport, Connecticut

   This answer is not correct because the Bridgeport bakers made pies. The Yale students who bought the pies came up with the idea for the sport.

   Ⓑ some students at Frisbie High School

   This answer is not correct because Frisbie High School is not mentioned in the article.

   ● some students at Yale University

   This answer is correct because the first sentence in paragraph 2 states, *"Some students at Yale University invented this sport."*

   Ⓓ Walter Morrison

   This answer is not correct because Walter Morrison made the first plastic Frisbees—he did not invent the sport.

4. Where were the first plastic Frisbees made?

   Ⓐ at Yale University

   This answer is not correct because a sentence in the last paragraph states, *"Walter Morrison and the Wham-O Manufacturing Company began making plastic models."*

   ● at the Wham-O Manufacturing Company

   This answer is correct because a sentence in the last paragraph states, *"Walter Morrison and the Wham-O Manufacturing Company began making plastic models."*

   Ⓒ at the Frisbie Bakery

   This answer is not correct because the pie pans from the Frisbie Bakery were made of metal, not plastic.

   Ⓓ at the Walter Morrison Manufacturing Company

   This answer is not correct because the article does not mention a company with that name. Walter Morrison worked with the Wham-O Manufacturing Company to make the first plastic Frisbees.

MORE TO KNOW

Writers use facts and details for many reasons. Facts and details make writing more interesting. When you read, look for sentences that

- describe a person, place, or thing.
- explain how to do something.
- tell the order in which things happen.
- share an experience, idea, or opinion.

Read this article about ancient Rome. Then answer the questions.

A Powerful Empire

Rome was once the center of a huge empire. The Roman Empire lasted hundreds of years. Romans ruled almost all of Europe, as well as parts of Africa and Asia. About 1,500 years ago, the Roman Empire fell apart.

Many Roman ideas still affect the way we live today. The Constitution of the United States of America is based on ideas in Roman laws. The alphabet we use is the Roman alphabet. Some of our months are named after Roman leaders. July is named after Julius Caesar. August is named in honor of Augustus Caesar, the first Roman emperor. Even the planets were named after Roman gods. Jupiter was the king of the gods. Mars was the god of war. And Venus was the goddess of love.

5. When did the Roman Empire end?
   - Ⓐ about 150 years ago
   - Ⓑ about 500 years ago
   - Ⓒ about 1,500 years ago
   - Ⓓ about 15,000 years ago

6. Which of these is a fact about the Roman Empire?
   - Ⓐ All of our months are named after Roman leaders.
   - Ⓑ Augustus Caesar created our alphabet.
   - Ⓒ The first Roman emperor was Julius Caesar.
   - Ⓓ Romans ruled almost all of Europe, as well as parts of Africa and Asia.

7. The planets were named after
   - Ⓐ Roman cities.
   - Ⓑ Roman emperors.
   - Ⓒ Roman gods.
   - Ⓓ Roman months.

8. Which detail tells more about the main idea of the first paragraph?
   - Ⓐ July is named after Julius Caesar.
   - Ⓑ The Roman Empire lasted hundreds of years.
   - Ⓒ The Constitution of the United States is based on ideas in Roman laws.
   - Ⓓ Many Roman ideas still affect the way we live today.

Read this Greek myth about a monster called the Sphinx. Then answer the questions.

Tell Me a Riddle

There once was a monster called the Sphinx. This beast had a woman's head, a lion's body, a serpent's tail, and an eagle's wings. The Sphinx lived on a mountaintop. Whenever travelers passed by, the creature asked them a riddle. Travelers who could not answer the riddle were killed and eaten by the Sphinx. No one had ever escaped being killed.

One day, a Greek prince named Oedipus came by. The Sphinx challenged Oedipus to answer her riddle.

Her riddle was: "What goes on four legs in the morning, two legs at noon, and three legs in the evening?"

Unlike other travelers, Oedipus quickly solved the riddle. "A human," he replied. "For we humans crawl on all fours as babies. We walk on two legs as adults. Then we use a cane when we are old and weak."

The Sphinx could not believe that Oedipus had answered correctly. The creature was so ashamed that she flung herself over a cliff.

9. What is one detail that tells about the Sphinx?
   - Ⓐ She was old and weak.
   - Ⓑ She had three legs.
   - Ⓒ She had a lion's body.
   - Ⓓ She had an eagle's head.

10. Who was Oedipus?
    - Ⓐ a Greek prince
    - Ⓑ an ordinary traveler
    - Ⓒ a Greek god
    - Ⓓ a monster in the form of a human

11. A detail that tells about the main idea of paragraph 4 is
    - Ⓐ Oedipus was challenged by the Sphinx.
    - Ⓑ the Sphinx had a serpent's tail.
    - Ⓒ the Sphinx lived on a mountaintop.
    - Ⓓ Oedipus quickly solved the riddle.

12. Which of these tells more about the main idea of the last paragraph?
    - Ⓐ The Sphinx was ashamed that Oedipus had solved the riddle.
    - Ⓑ Oedipus took his time answering the riddle.
    - Ⓒ Oedipus was afraid of the Sphinx.
    - Ⓓ Travelers who could not answer the riddle were eaten by the Sphinx.

TEST TIPS	• A test question about facts and details may ask you about something that is stated in a reading passage. • A test question about facts and details may ask you about the *who, what, where, when, why,* and *how* of the main idea.

Read this article about measurement. Then answer questions about the article. Choose the best answer for Numbers 13 and 14.

Measuring Tools

We use many different kinds of tools to measure things. Rulers, tape measures, and yardsticks measure length. Clocks, watches, and hourglasses measure time. Calendars measure time, too, but in days and months, not minutes and hours.

Scales measure weight. Thermometers measure temperature. And protractors measure angles of common shapes.

A speedometer measures a vehicle's speed. An odometer measures the distance that the vehicle travels. For walkers, a pedometer can measure the number of steps they take.

Some people think that even intelligence can be measured. They use an IQ test. Still, tools can't be used to measure everything. For example, how would you measure happiness or friendship?

13. An odometer is used to measure
- Ⓐ length.
- Ⓑ time.
- Ⓒ speed.
- Ⓓ distance.

14. What tool measures weight?
- Ⓐ hourglass
- Ⓑ scale
- Ⓒ protractor
- Ⓓ pedometer

Read this story about a girl who wants a pet. Then answer questions about the story. Choose the best answer for Numbers 15 and 16.

A Pet Platypus

All of Lang's friends had pets. Samantha had a dog; Claire had a cat; and Theo had a parakeet. Lang wanted a pet, too, but she wanted something unusual. She looked through some animal books for ideas. Finally, she saw an Australian mammal she liked. The animal was funny looking. It had a snout like a duck's bill, webbed feet, and a broad, flat tail. Lang had decided to get a platypus.

Lang begged her parents to get her a pet platypus for her birthday. Of course, her mom and dad had all kinds of objections.

"But Lang," they protested, "a platypus needs to swim in rivers and streams."

"It can swim in our bathtub," Lang replied.

"How will you feed it?" they added. "A platypus mostly eats insects and worms."

Lang answered, "Then the yard will get a good cleaning."

On the morning of Lang's birthday, her parents walked into her room. They were carrying a big wrapped box. Lang opened the gift and laughed. Inside the box was a life-size platypus. It was plastic, just right for swimming in the bathtub.

15. What is one fact about a platypus?
- Ⓐ It has a duck's tail.
- Ⓑ It has webbed feet.
- Ⓒ It has a snout like a dog.
- Ⓓ It has feathers.

16. Which of these is a fact from the story?
- Ⓐ A platypus can be purchased at a pet store.
- Ⓑ Lang wanted an unusual pet.
- Ⓒ Lang already had a pet dog.
- Ⓓ Lang's parents did not think a plastic platypus was a good idea.

What Is Sequence?

Many stories you read are told in order. A fiction book usually tells what happens first, next, and so on. A nonfiction book usually tells about events in the order in which they happened. In both kinds of writing, authors use sequence to tell about what happens.

1 Write three events in your life that were special to you.

_____

_____

_____

2 List these events in the order in which they happened. Number each item.

_____

_____

_____

Work with a Partner

- Tell your partner about one of your favorite fiction books or movies.
- Take turns describing what happens in the book or movie.
  Tell about the beginning, the middle, and the ending.
- Try to use only one sentence to describe each part.

- Use specific evidence from stories to relate a sequence of events (**GPI.R.2**)
- Understand written directions and procedures (**GPI.R.1**)
- Use knowledge of story structure to interpret stories (**GPI.R.2**)

How Do You Find Sequence?

You can find the order in which things happen in a story by thinking about the beginning, the middle, and the ending. You can also look for words that tell about sequence. Some of these clue words are *first, next,* and *then.* Other clue words that tell about sequence are words about time and days of the week.

Read this passage about a friend who is moving. Look for clue words that tell you the sequence of the story.

> My friend Tasha is moving tomorrow. Today we went to lunch at the Pizza Barn and spent our last day together. Tonight she is sleeping over at my house. I hope the morning comes slowly.

1. Let's think about the order in which things are happening in the story.

2. Look at the chart below.
   It shows the order of events in the story.

3. Fill in the missing information from the story that tells what is happening tomorrow.

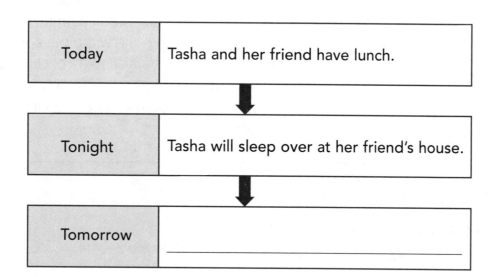

Today	Tasha and her friend have lunch.
Tonight	Tasha will sleep over at her friend's house.
Tomorrow	_____

WHAT TO KNOW	The order in which things happen in a reading passage is called **sequence**. Sequence tells what happens first, second, third, and so on.

- Clue words such as *first, next, then, last, finally, before,* and *after* often tell the order in which things happen.
- Clues such as times of day, days of the week, months, and years tell when things happen.
- Sometimes, there are no clue words. Thinking about the beginning, the middle, and the ending of a reading passage will help you understand the order in which things happen.

Read this story about how Tara prepared for a speech. As you read, think about the order in which things happen in the story.

Speak Up!

Tara was nervous about presenting a speech to her entire class. So she made sure she was well prepared. On Monday, Tara chose a topic for her speech. On Tuesday, she gathered information about her topic. On Wednesday, she wrote the speech. She gave it an introduction, a body, and a conclusion. On Thursday, Tara copied her speech onto note cards. Finally, on Friday, she practiced her speech until she felt ready to present it.

The order in which things happen in the story is:

On Monday, Tara chose a topic for her speech.

On Tuesday, she gathered information about her topic.

On Wednesday, she wrote the speech.

On Thursday, Tara copied her speech onto note cards.

Finally, on Friday, she practiced her speech until she felt ready to present it.

Read these directions to a number trick. As you read, think about what to do first, second, and so on. Then answer the questions.

Math Magic

Here is a fun number trick that's easy to solve. Just follow the directions carefully. First, think of a number. Second, double the number, and add two. Third, multiply the result by three. The next step is to add three. Then subtract your original number. After you do that, subtract four from the answer. Then subtract five. Finally, divide by five. Did you end up with the number with which you began?

1. What do you do first to solve the number trick?
   Ⓐ Double the number.
   Ⓑ Add three.
   Ⓒ Subtract five.
   Ⓓ Think of a number.

2. In the directions, which clue word tells what to do last?
   Ⓐ then
   Ⓑ third
   Ⓒ finally
   Ⓓ next

Work with a Partner

- Talk about your answers to the questions.
- Tell why you chose your answers.
- Then talk about what you have learned so far about understanding sequence.

REVIEW

Sequence tells the order in which things happen.

- Look for clue words such as *first, next, then, last, finally, before,* and *after.* These clue words often tell the order in which things happen.

- Look for clues that tell about times of day, days of the week, months, or years.

- When there are no clue words, think about the beginning, the middle, and the ending of the reading passage. This will help you understand the order in which things happen.

Read this story about a birthday game played in New Zealand. As you read, ask yourself, "What happens first? What happens next? What happened after that?" Then answer the questions.

A Birthday in New Zealand

Because of his mom's job, Luke and his family had moved from Texas to New Zealand for a year. Luke had been living in New Zealand only a few weeks when his new friend, Joshua, invited him to his birthday party. Luke wondered how the party might be different from those back home.

It didn't take long to find out. After Joshua opened his presents, his friends lined up in two teams to play a popular birthday game. Joshua stood at the front of one line. Luke stood in line a few players back so he could watch and learn the game. Each team was positioned in front of a small table. On each of the tables were a hat, a pair of gloves, a plastic knife, a pile of forks, and a chocolate cake.

First, the players at the front of each line raced to their table. Then they pulled on the gloves and slapped the hat on their head. Next, they cut a piece of cake. Luke noticed that players could cut large pieces, but they had to use a fork to eat every crumb before progressing to the next step. Last, they took off the hat and gloves and ran to the end of the line.

Sophie went after Joshua. Luke was the third player, followed by Elle, Max, and James. Anya went last. The other team finished its cake first, but Luke didn't care. He thought the game was hilarious, and he couldn't wait to teach it to his friends back in Texas next November.

3. Just after Sophie took her turn,
   Ⓐ Joshua ran to the end of the line.
   Ⓑ Luke took his turn.
   Ⓒ the other team finished its cake.
   Ⓓ Anya took her turn.

4. Which clue word in the story tells what the second step of the game is?
   Ⓐ before
   Ⓑ next
   Ⓒ then
   Ⓓ November

Which Answer Is Correct and Why?

Look at the answer choices for each question.
Read why each answer choice is correct or not correct.

3. Just after Sophie took her turn,

   Ⓐ **Joshua ran to the end of the line.**

   This answer is not correct because the story states that Joshua was the first person in line. He ran to the end of the line before Sophie took her turn.

   ● **Luke took his turn.**

   This answer is correct because the story states that Sophie went after Joshua. Joshua was the first player, which would make Sophie the second player. The story states that Luke was the third player, so he had to be the player after Sophie.

   Ⓒ **the other team finished its cake.**

   This answer is not correct because the story states that Luke, Elle, Max, James, and Anya all had turns after Sophie. This means that the other team was still racing to finish just after Sophie took her turn.

   Ⓓ **Anya took her turn.**

   This answer is not correct because the story states that Anya went last. Luke, Elle, Max, and James all went between Sophie and Anya.

4. Which clue word in the story tells what the second step of the game is?

   Ⓐ **before**

   This answer is not correct because this clue word is not used in the selection.

   Ⓑ **next**

   This answer is not correct because the first step is that players raced to the table. The second step is that they put on gloves and hats. The step after that is the third step, which begins with the clue word *next*.

   ● **then**

   This answer is correct because it begins the sentence that tells what happens after the first step of the game when players raced to the table. The second step then follows when players put on gloves and hats.

   Ⓓ **November**

   This answer is not correct because it is not included in the paragraph that describes the steps of the game.

MORE TO KNOW

Many reading passages tell details and events in the order in which they happened. Look for sequence in these kinds of reading passages:

- directions
- journal entries
- history articles
- newspaper stories
- stories, fables, and folktales
- autobiographies and biographies

Read this fable by Aesop. Then answer the questions.

The Fox and the Crow

A crow was sitting on a branch of a tree. She held a piece of cheese in her beak. A fox caught sight of the crow and began thinking of a way to get the cheese. He went and stood under the tree and looked up. "What a noble bird I see above me!" he said. "Her beauty is without equal. The colors of her feathers are so pleasing. If only her voice were as sweet as her looks are fair. She ought, without doubt, to be queen of the birds."

Now, the crow was greatly flattered by this praise. Just to show the fox that she could sing, she gave a loud caw. Down came the cheese, of course.

The fox snatched up the cheese and said, "You do have a lovely voice, I see. But what you want is wits."

5. Which of these happened first?
   Ⓐ The fox stood under a tree.
   Ⓑ The fox began thinking of a way to get the crow's cheese.
   Ⓒ A fox saw a crow in a tree.
   Ⓓ The fox praised the crow's beauty.

6. Just after the crow gave a loud caw,
   Ⓐ the cheese came down.
   Ⓑ the fox praised the crow's voice.
   Ⓒ the fox snatched up the cheese.
   Ⓓ the fox told the crow she needed wits.

7. Which clue word in the story tells what the fox did last?
   Ⓐ after
   Ⓑ last
   Ⓒ finally
   Ⓓ There is no clue word.

8. What did the fox do before snatching up the cheese?
   Ⓐ He sang a sweet song.
   Ⓑ He said the crow ought to be queen of the birds.
   Ⓒ He climbed the tree.
   Ⓓ He scolded the crow.

Read this autobiography of a folk heroine. Then answer the questions.

The Life and Adventures of Calamity Jane

My maiden name was Martha Jane Canary. I was born in Princeton, Missouri, on May 1, 1852. As a child, I always had a fondness for adventure and outdoor exercise. I began to ride horses at an early age. In time, I became an expert rider.

In 1865, our family moved to Virginia City, Montana. It took us five months to make the journey. On the way, I spent most of my time hunting with the men. I was considered a remarkably good shot for a girl of my age.

Mother died in 1866, and I left Montana for Utah. I remained in Utah until 1867, when my father died. In 1870, I joined General Custer as a scout in Wyoming. When I joined Custer, I donned the uniform of a soldier. I soon got to be perfectly at home in men's clothes.

As a scout, I performed a great many dangerous missions. In 1873, we were ordered to crush an Indian revolt. Our commander, Captain Egan, was shot. I galloped to his side in time to catch him as he was falling from his saddle. I lifted him onto my horse and got him safely to the fort. On recovering, Captain Egan said, "I name you Calamity Jane, the heroine of the plains." I have borne that name up to the present time.

9. In the autobiography, clues that tell about the sequence are
   - Ⓐ times of day.
   - Ⓑ days of the week.
   - Ⓒ months.
   - Ⓓ years.

10. What happened in Calamity Jane's life during the year 1867?
    - Ⓐ Her mother died.
    - Ⓑ Her father died.
    - Ⓒ She became a scout.
    - Ⓓ She earned her nickname.

11. When did Calamity Jane go to Wyoming?
    - Ⓐ 1852
    - Ⓑ 1865
    - Ⓒ 1870
    - Ⓓ 1873

12. What happened just after Captain Egan was shot?
    - Ⓐ He nicknamed the woman who saved him.
    - Ⓑ He arrived at the fort.
    - Ⓒ Calamity Jane galloped to his side.
    - Ⓓ Calamity Jane lifted him onto her horse.

TEST TIPS

- A test question about sequence may ask you when certain things happen in a reading passage.
- A test question about sequence may ask you to put events from a reading passage in order.
- A test question about sequence may contain words such as *first, second, last, before,* or *after.*

Read these directions for making a flip book. Then answer questions about the directions. Choose the best answer for Numbers 13 and 14.

Have you ever wondered how cartoons are made? Special artists called animators create cartoons. To make a short cartoon, animators must draw thousands of pictures. In each picture, the characters are drawn in a slightly different position. When the drawings pass very quickly before the viewers' eyes, the characters seem to move.

You can see how this works by making a flip book. To begin, cut a sheet of stiff paper into 25 or 30 small rectangles, all the same size.

Next, choose a simple movement to draw, such as running, kicking, or jumping. Ask a friend to model the movement for you. Have your friend hold different poses while you draw a quick sketch on each rectangle. Keep the drawings simple by using stick figures. Also, make sure that you draw each sketch in the same spot on each page. Leave space on the left-hand side to staple the pictures together. It's a good idea to number the back of each drawing.

When you are done, put the pictures in the correct order and staple them together. Then hold the book in your left hand. Flip the pages of the book with your right hand as fast as you can. As you do this, your stick figure will appear to move.

13. Which step is done second to make a flip book?

Ⓐ Draw stick figures.

Ⓑ Ask a friend to model poses.

Ⓒ Cut paper into rectangles.

Ⓓ Choose a simple movement to draw.

14. The boxes show some of the steps in making a flip book.

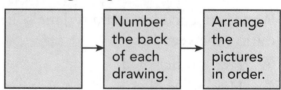

What belongs in the empty box?

Ⓐ Flip the pages quickly.

Ⓑ Draw simple sketches.

Ⓒ Hold the book in one hand.

Ⓓ Staple the pictures together.

32 Understanding Sequence

Read this article about how a knight gets dressed for battle. Then answer questions about the article. Choose the best answer for Numbers 15 and 16.

From 1100 to 1300, great castles were built all over Europe. Kings and powerful lords built the castles to defend their lands from enemies. Hundreds of knights lived in the castles. They fought for the kings and lords. A knight had to be well trained and always ready for battle. A knight also had to dress well for his job. His life depended on the heavy suit of armor he wore.

A knight couldn't dress himself. A squire had to help him. A squire was a boy who was training to be a knight. First, the knight dressed in a loose shirt and long leg coverings. Second, he put a padded tunic over his shirt and a padded cap on his head. Over the padded tunic, the knight put on a chain-mail shirt. Chain mail is made of small iron rings linked together. The knight then added a chain-mail hood and leggings.

Next, the squire strapped metal guards onto the knight's chest, legs, arms, and shoulders. The squire then pulled a cloth tunic over the knight's armor. This tunic kept the metal armor from rusting in the rain. The tunic bore a special design, called a coat of arms, to show who the knight was.

After the tunic was on, the squire covered the knight's head and face with a metal helmet. The squire also pulled metal gloves over the knight's hands and placed spurs at his heels. Last, the squire handed the knight his sword, lance, and shield. Finally, the knight was ready to climb onto his horse and ride off into to battle.

15. What did a knight put on before his chain mail?
  Ⓐ a metal chest guard
  Ⓑ a padded tunic
  Ⓒ a tunic with a coat of arms
  Ⓓ metal gloves

16. After the cloth tunic was pulled over the knight's armor, the squire added
  Ⓐ metal leg and arm guards.
  Ⓑ a padded cap.
  Ⓒ a metal helmet.
  Ⓓ long leg coverings.

Read this letter written by Elizabeth Blackwell. Then answer questions about the letter. Choose the best answer for Numbers 1 through 6.

June 24, 1863

Dear Emily,

Thank you for your lovely letter. I'm flattered that you'd like to follow in my footsteps. Here are the answers to the questions you asked me.

I was born in England in 1821. My family moved to America when I was 11. My father died six years later, and I had to go to work. So, I became a teacher. Teaching was one of the few jobs a woman could have at that time.

I decided to become a doctor in 1844, after visiting a dying friend. She told me that I was clever and should consider studying medicine. I reminded her that there were no women doctors in the United States. She replied that she might not be dying if a woman doctor had treated her.

I continued teaching to earn the money for medical school. The principal of my school was a kind doctor named Samuel Dickson. He encouraged me and gave me his medical books to study.

When I applied to medical schools, 28 schools turned me down. I had almost given up hope. But, at last, the Geneva Medical College, in New York, said yes.

Being the only woman in a class of 150 men was difficult. When I graduated in 1849, though, I was first in my class. I was also the first woman in the United States to receive a medical degree.

I have one main purpose as a doctor. I want to teach women how to care for themselves and their children. I opened a clinic for them. It now includes a medical college for women. Maybe you'd like to apply there someday.

I wish you all the best.

Sincerely,
Elizabeth Blackwell

Finding Main Idea

1. What is this letter mostly about?
   - Ⓐ the life of Elizabeth Blackwell
   - Ⓑ women's job choices in the 1800s
   - Ⓒ an early death of a good friend
   - Ⓓ getting into medical school

Recalling Facts and Details

4. Who first inspired Elizabeth Blackwell to become a doctor?
   - Ⓐ her father
   - Ⓑ a dying friend
   - Ⓒ Samuel Dickson
   - Ⓓ the teachers at Geneva Medical College

Finding Main Idea

2. A good title for this selection is
   - Ⓐ "Surviving Medical School."
   - Ⓑ "The First Woman Doctor."
   - Ⓒ "A Teacher's Life."
   - Ⓓ "Making a Promise."

Understanding Sequence

5. Which of these happened first?
   - Ⓐ Blackwell got turned down by 28 medical schools.
   - Ⓑ Blackwell taught to earn money for medical school.
   - Ⓒ Blackwell opened a women's clinic.
   - Ⓓ Blackwell entered Geneva Medical College.

Recalling Facts and Details

3. Elizabeth Blackwell came to the United States at the age of
   - Ⓐ 6.
   - Ⓑ 24.
   - Ⓒ 29.
   - Ⓓ 11.

Understanding Sequence

6. You can tell the sequence in the letter mostly by
   - Ⓐ looking for clues that tell about days, months, or years.
   - Ⓑ thinking about the main idea.
   - Ⓒ finding facts and details.
   - Ⓓ thinking about the beginning, the middle, and the ending.

Read this story from Syria. Then answer questions about the story. Choose the best answer for Numbers 7 through 12.

There was once a rich businessman who bought ten donkeys to lend out for hire. The first day, he hired out his donkeys to a wood gatherer. At night, the wood gatherer returned the donkeys and paid the businessman his money.

On the road to his tent, it occurred to the businessman to count the donkeys. He found there were only nine, for he did not count the one on which he was sitting.

"The wood gatherer stole one of my animals!" he cried.

He got off the donkey in a rage and counted all over again. Now there were ten.

"The wood gatherer did not cheat me after all," he thought.

He rode on, and it occurred to him to count the animals again. He did, and again there were only nine. Once more, he did not have the understanding to count the one on which he was sitting.

"That thieving wood gatherer took one of my donkeys."

The angry man leapt out of his saddle and counted the animals all over again. And again there were ten.

"I accused the wood gatherer wrongfully. All the animals are here."

So the man got on his donkey and rode on. But he had no peace. He could not understand why there should be a different number of donkeys each time he counted them.

"Whenever I mount my donkey, I lose one. When I get off, the beast comes back. I think I'd better stay off altogether, because next time I mount my donkey, I may lose one for certain."

So the man walked the long distance to his home on foot.

Finding Main Idea

7. The main idea of the story is found
   Ⓐ in the first paragraph.
   Ⓑ in the middle of the story.
   Ⓒ in the last paragraph.
   Ⓓ by thinking about the most important idea in the story.

Recalling Facts and Details

10. Which detail tells that the man was angry?
   Ⓐ He got off his donkey in a rage.
   Ⓑ He did not count the donkey on which he was sitting.
   Ⓒ He couldn't understand why his count was different each time.
   Ⓓ He rode on toward his tent.

Finding Main Idea

8. Which of these is the best title for this story?
   Ⓐ "Ten Counting Donkeys"
   Ⓑ "A Rich Man Poor in Understanding"
   Ⓒ "A Clever Thief"
   Ⓓ "The Long Journey Home on Foot"

Understanding Sequence

11. Which of these happened last?
   Ⓐ The man leapt out of his saddle.
   Ⓑ The standing man counted ten donkeys.
   Ⓒ The man thought he should stay off his donkey altogether.
   Ⓓ The man was sorry that he called the wood gatherer a thief.

Recalling Facts and Details

9. Who hired the man's donkeys?
   Ⓐ a thief
   Ⓑ a woodcutter
   Ⓒ a wood gatherer
   Ⓓ a businessman

Understanding Sequence

12. The boxes tell some things that happened in the story.

The man hired out ten donkeys.		The man counted nine donkeys.
1	2	3

Which of these belongs in box 2?
   Ⓐ The man counted ten donkeys.
   Ⓑ The man got off his donkey.
   Ⓒ The donkeys were returned by the wood gatherer.
   Ⓓ The man thought that a donkey had been stolen.

What Is Cause and Effect?

There is a reason for everything that happens. What happens is called the *effect*.
Why it happens is called the *cause*.

1 Write what happens if you oversleep on a school day.

_____

_____

_____

_____

2 Write why this happens.

_____

_____

_____

_____

Work with a Partner

- Take turns giving each other examples of cause and effect. You might say, "I watered the plant because its leaves were drooping."
- In each example, tell which part is the cause and which part is the effect.

- Use knowledge of story structure to interpret stories (**GPI.R.2**)
- Use evidence from stories to identify themes, actions, motivations (**GPI.R.2**)

How Do You Find Cause and Effect?

Many reading passages include examples of cause and effect. You can find causes and effects by thinking about what happens in a passage and why.

Read this passage about Marcus and Jake. Think about the things that happen and why they happen.

> Marcus and Jake were hiking along a mountain path. They came to a fork in the trail, and they didn't know which way to go.
>
> "Look at the map," said Marcus to Jake. Jake checked his pockets and his backpack, but he couldn't find the map.
>
> "I left it at the last place we stopped to rest. We'll have to go back to find it," said Jake.

1. Let's find an example of cause and effect in the passage.

2. Look at the two boxes below.

   The first box tells what happened. This is the *effect*.

   The second box tells why it happened. This is the *cause*.

What happened? (effect)	Why did it happen? (cause)
Marcus and Jake didn't know which way to go on the trail.	Jake couldn't find the map.

3. Let's find another example of cause and effect in the passage.

   Look at the two boxes below.

   The first box tells the cause for why something happened.

4. Fill in the effect in the second box. Tell what happened because Jake left the map behind.

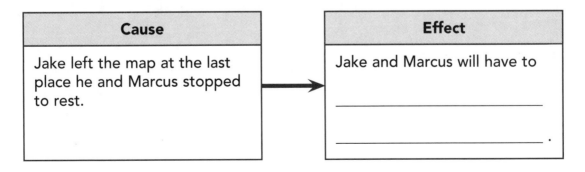

Cause	Effect
Jake left the map at the last place he and Marcus stopped to rest.	Jake and Marcus will have to _____ _____ .

WHAT TO KNOW

What happens and why is called **cause and effect**.
Why something happens is the **cause**.
What happens because of the cause is the **effect**.

- A cause is the reason that something happens.

- An effect is what happens as a result of the cause.

- Clue words such as *so, so that, since, because,* and *if* often signal cause and effect. Other clue words are *reason* and *as a result*.

Read this article about birds that don't fly. As you read, think about one thing that happened to some types of birds and why.

All birds have wings, but not all birds fly. Scientists believe that there once was a time when all birds could fly. In time, however, some types of birds no longer needed to fly in order to survive. So these birds became flightless. The two most common types of flightless birds are penguins and ostriches.

Penguins have flippers instead of wings. They use their flippers to help them swim underwater at fast speeds. Ostriches also move quickly, even though they are the largest birds on Earth. Their wings help them balance as they run. These birds can run at speeds up to 35 miles per hour.

One thing that happened to some types of birds and why is:

What happened: **They became flightless.**

Why it happened: **They no longer needed to fly in order to survive.**

Read this journal entry written by a girl named Hannah. As you read, look for clue words to help you understand what happens and why it happens. Then answer the questions.

January 15

Today my parents took me to an art museum. The museum was exhibiting the paintings of Vincent van Gogh, a Dutch painter of the late 1800s. Because I like to paint, my parents thought I would enjoy seeing van Gogh's work. I just thought I'd be bored.

Boy, was I ever surprised! The minute I walked into the van Gogh gallery, I was fascinated. Van Gogh used bold, bright colors to express his feelings about what he saw. I spent hours looking at van Gogh's vivid paintings. When it was finally time to leave, I was disappointed. My parents had to drag me away because I was having such a good time.

1. Hannah's parents thought she would enjoy seeing van Gogh's work because she
   - Ⓐ likes art museums.
   - Ⓑ has always enjoyed van Gogh's work.
   - Ⓒ likes to paint.
   - Ⓓ had nothing else to do.

2. Which clue word or words in the journal entry signals the reason that Hannah's parents had to drag her away?
   - Ⓐ so that
   - Ⓑ because
   - Ⓒ since
   - Ⓓ if

Work with a Partner

- Talk about your answers to the questions.
- Tell why you chose your answers.
- Then talk about what you have learned so far about recognizing cause and effect.

REVIEW	What happens and why is called cause and effect. • To find a cause, look for a reason that something happened. Ask yourself, "*Why* did it happen?" • To find an effect, look for a result, or something that happened. Ask yourself, "*What* happened?" • Look for clue words that signal cause and effect, such as *so, so that, since, because, if, reason*, and *as a result*.

Read this silly poem. As you read, ask yourself, "What are some things that happen in the poem? Why do these things happen?" Then answer the questions.

A silly young girl had a dream in her head,
Her dream was to sleep on a big feather bed.
She thought, "Feathers are light and soft as a breeze.
I'd sure like to sleep on a bed made of these!"
So she spread some goose feathers on a flat rock.
She had happened to find them on a boat dock.
She lay down on the feathers and tried to sleep.
But the bed was so hard she wanted to weep!
Soon she felt pains in her knees, neck, and head.
"Feather beds are hard! I don't want one!" she said.

3. Why did the silly girl want to sleep on a feather bed?
   Ⓐ She knew that feathers were soft.
   Ⓑ She had a dream about feathers.
   Ⓒ Her friend had a feather bed.
   Ⓓ She had pains in her knees.

4. The silly girl wanted to sleep on a bed of feathers, so she
   Ⓐ bought a mattress made of feathers.
   Ⓑ plucked feathers off a goose.
   Ⓒ slept on a dock covered with feathers.
   Ⓓ spread feathers on a flat rock.

Which Answer Is Correct and Why?

Look at the answer choices for each question.
Read why each answer choice is correct or not correct.

3. Why did the silly girl want to sleep on a feather bed?

● **She knew that feathers were soft.**
This answer is correct because the girl thinks to herself, *"Feathers are light and soft as a breeze. I'd sure like to sleep on a bed made of these!"*

Ⓑ **She had a dream about feathers.**
This answer is not correct because the girl had a dream of sleeping on a big feather bed, not a dream about feathers.

Ⓒ **Her friend had a feather bed.**
This answer is not correct because nothing is said in the poem about a friend with a feather bed.

Ⓓ **She had pains in her knees.**
This answer is not correct because the pains in the girl's knees are caused by lying on the hard rock. Having pains in her knees was not the reason for her wanting to sleep on a feather bed.

4. The silly girl wanted to sleep on a bed of feathers, so she

Ⓐ **bought a mattress made of feathers.**
This answer is not correct because the girl does not buy a mattress of any kind.

Ⓑ **plucked feathers off a goose.**
This answer is not correct because the girl does not pluck feathers off a goose. The poem says that she had found goose feathers on a dock.

Ⓒ **slept on a dock covered with feathers.**
This answer is not correct because the girl does not sleep on a dock. She finds feathers on a dock and spreads them on a flat rock.

● **spread feathers on a flat rock.**
This answer is correct because the effect is stated directly in the poem (she spread feathers on a flat rock) after the cause (she wanted to sleep on a bed made of feathers). The clue word *So* in the poem signals this cause-and-effect relationship.

| MORE TO KNOW | Sometimes, there are no clue words to signal cause and effect in a reading passage. When there are no clue words, do the following: |

- To find an effect, think about *what* happened.
- To find a cause, think about *how* or *why* it happened.
- Think about what you already know about how one thing might cause another thing to happen.

Read this article about a spring holiday. Then answer the questions.

April Fool's Day

On April 1, people like to play jokes on one another. This day is called April Fools' Day. No one is sure how this custom to fool people began. Some people think the tradition began in France. Until the mid-1500s there, April 1 had been the first day of the new year. The calendar was changed in 1564. The first day of the new year was moved to January 1. Some people, though, still celebrated New Year's Day on April 1. Others made fun of them for celebrating the new year on the wrong day. They called these people "April fools."

When the new year had begun on April 1, people gave gifts to one another. After the new calendar changed New Year's Day to January 1, some people still gave presents on April 1. But they chose joke gifts. As a result, people came to play jokes on one another on April Fools' Day.

5. How did people come to play jokes on one another on April Fools' Day?
   - Ⓐ They were not allowed to give gifts on this day.
   - Ⓑ They once gave joke gifts to one another on this day.
   - Ⓒ It was a French custom to play jokes on this day.
   - Ⓓ They wanted to act like fools.

6. Which clue word or phrase in the article signals the reason that people play jokes on April 1?
   - Ⓐ since
   - Ⓑ so
   - Ⓒ as a result
   - Ⓓ because

7. When the calendar was changed in 1564,
   - Ⓐ January 1 became New Year's Day.
   - Ⓑ April 1 became New Year's Day.
   - Ⓒ the month of January was dropped from the calendar.
   - Ⓓ people began acting like fools.

8. Why were people called "April fools"?
   - Ⓐ Before 1564, they celebrated the new year on April 1.
   - Ⓑ They liked to give joke gifts in April.
   - Ⓒ They thought that January 1 began the new year.
   - Ⓓ After 1564, they continued to celebrate April 1 as New Year's Day.

Read this brochure for a unique tourist attraction. Then answer the questions.

Looking for things to do in San Jose, California? Why not visit the city's largest house? The Winchester House is fun to visit because of its unusual history and uncommon style.

The Winchester House was once an eight-room farmhouse. It was built by Oliver Winchester, the inventor of the Winchester rifle. Oliver died in 1886. His widow, Sarah, felt great sorrow. She went to see a woman who claimed she could speak with the dead. She told Sarah that spirits of people killed by her husband's rifles were angry. The spirits were a danger to Sarah. There was only one way for Sarah to avoid danger. She must keep adding on to her house.

Over the next 36 years, the Winchester House grew and changed. Carpenters worked 24 hours a day. To keep them busy, Sarah often ordered them to build useless features. Many doors opened to blank walls. Some staircases led nowhere.

Building didn't stop on the Winchester House until Sarah's death in 1922. By then, the house had become a mansion seven stories high with 160 rooms.

9. What happened as a result of Sarah's visit to the woman who claimed she could speak with the dead?
   Ⓐ Sarah talked to her dead husband.
   Ⓑ Sarah began adding on to her house.
   Ⓒ Sarah ignored the woman's advice.
   Ⓓ Winchester rifles were no longer made.

10. Why did Sarah add useless features to her house?
   Ⓐ to keep the carpenters busy
   Ⓑ to anger the spirits of the dead
   Ⓒ to make the house more mysterious
   Ⓓ to please tourists

11. Construction on the Winchester House stopped because
   Ⓐ the carpenters had finished the job.
   Ⓑ Sarah could no longer afford to keep adding on.
   Ⓒ the house had become a popular tourist attraction.
   Ⓓ Sarah had died.

12. One reason the Winchester House is a fun place to visit is that
   Ⓐ it is haunted.
   Ⓑ it is unusually small.
   Ⓒ it has an unusual history.
   Ⓓ it is the largest house in California.

TEST TIPS

- A test question about cause and effect may ask you *what* happened in a reading passage (the effect).

- A test question about cause and effect may ask you *why* something happened (the cause).

- A test question about cause and effect often contains words such as *because, why, reason,* or *what happened.*

Read this story from Mexico. Then answer questions about the story. Choose the best answer for Numbers 13 and 14.

Twelve on a Bench

One day, the people of Lagos got into a great argument. Finally, they asked the twelve oldest and wisest men of Lagos for their help. The men decided to meet on the bench in the town square to discuss the matter.

Six of the men arrived first. Each man wore a big, wide sombrero. It was a hot day, so the six men took off their straw hats. As they sat down, they put the hats right next to them. The hats took up more space than the men did, so the bench was full.

Soon, the other six men came. They tried to sit down, but there wasn't any space.

"There is no room on the bench for us," said one of the men standing.

"I think the bench has shrunk," answered one of those sitting.

"Why don't we try to stretch the bench?" suggested the oldest man.

So the six sitting on the bench arose, put their sombreros on their heads, and got hold of one end of the bench. Then the six standing got hold of the other end of the bench, and each group began pulling the wood as hard as they could. After some time, they put the bench down.

All twelve men sat down, each with his sombrero on his head. Of course, now the hats took up no space, and there was plenty of room for all.

"Now that we have done a fine job of stretching that bench, we can discuss our problem," spoke the oldest. So the men of Lagos, feeling very pleased with themselves, went on with their discussion.

13. Why did the first six men take off their hats?

Ⓐ They were being polite.

Ⓑ Their straw hats were itchy.

Ⓒ It was too hot to wear the hats.

Ⓓ The other six men asked them to.

14. What happened to the bench as a result of being pulled?

Ⓐ The bench became longer.

Ⓑ The bench stayed the same size.

Ⓒ The bench became shorter.

Ⓓ The bench broke in half.

Read this article about the human body. Then answer questions about the article. Choose the best answer for Numbers 15 and 16.

The Wonders of the Human Body

How the human body works is a mystery to most people. For example, do you know why you blink? Or blush? Or sneeze? For every bodily mystery, there is a scientific answer.

Everyone blinks—thousands of times a day. Blinking is important because it washes tears over the eyeballs. These tears clean away dirt and dust. If you stopped blinking, the outer covering of your eyeballs would dry out and get infected. You might even go blind.

Blushing can be embarrassing, but there's nothing you can do to stop it. People usually blush when someone teases or threatens them. One part of the brain sends out a message, and the body is told to get ready to defend itself. So extra blood flows to the muscles. When blood rushes to your arms and legs, no one notices it. But there's no hiding the redness in your face.

Sneezing is the way your body protects your lungs. If dust sneaks past your nose to the throat, the brain sends out an alarm. This warning causes the tubes in the throat to tighten so that the dust can't get through to the lungs. But when you try to breathe, pressure builds up in the narrow tubes. When the pressure becomes too great, the tubes are forced open with a quick blast of air. Achooo!

15. Blinking is important because it
    Ⓐ prevents pressure from building up behind the eyes.
    Ⓑ tells the body to get ready to defend itself.
    Ⓒ helps the body protect the lungs.
    Ⓓ cleans away dirt and dust from the eyes.

16. What usually happens when people are teased or threatened?
    Ⓐ They blink.
    Ⓑ They blush.
    Ⓒ They sneeze.
    Ⓓ They hiccup.

What Is Comparing and Contrasting?

Thinking about the ways two or more things are alike is called *comparing*.
Thinking about the ways two or more things are different is called *contrasting*.

1 Write three things you and a friend or family member have in common.

_____

_____

_____

_____

2 Write three things that you and the same friend or family member do not have in common.

_____

_____

_____

_____

Work with a Partner

- Take turns telling each other something that is the same about both of you.
- Then tell something that is different about both of you.
- See how many likenesses and differences you can find.

- Compare and contrast information on one topic from two different sources (**GPI.R.1**)
- Use knowledge of story structure to interpret stories (**GPI.R.2**)
- Compare and contrast characters, plot, and setting in literary works (**GPI.R.3**)
- Use evidence from stories to identify themes, actions, motivations (**GPI.R.2**)

How Do You Find Likenesses and Differences?

Many reading passages compare and contrast two or more things. You can find examples of comparing and contrasting by thinking about the details you read.

Read this passage about elephants. Think about how the two kinds of elephants are alike and how they are different.

> There are two kinds of elephants. Some elephants come from Africa. Other elephants come from India. Both animals are quite large, but African elephants are a bit larger than Indian elephants. The ears of Indian elephants are about half the size of those of African elephants. Both elephants have trunks that are long and strong.

1. Let's think about the details that tell about the likenesses between African elephants and Indian elephants.

   Now think about the details that tell about the differences between them.

2. Look at the diagram below.

   The shaded part of the first circle tells how African elephants are different from Indian elephants. The shaded part of the second circle tells how Indian elephants are different from African elephants. These are examples of *contrasting*.

   The information where the circles overlap tells how both kinds of elephants are alike. This is *comparing*.

3. Fill in the missing information where the circles overlap to tell another way in which both kinds of elephants are alike.

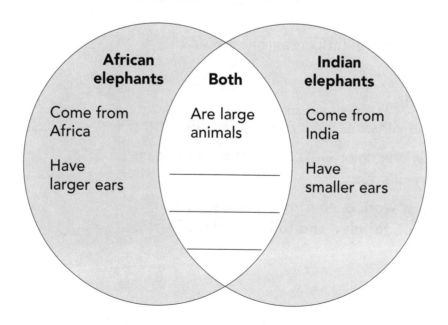

WHAT TO KNOW	Finding how two or more things are alike and how they are different is called **comparing and contrasting**. Comparing is finding how things are alike. Contrasting is finding how things are different.

- Clue words that signal how things are alike are *both, same, like, alike,* and *similar*.
- Clue words that signal how things are different are *but, unlike, different, however,* and *whereas*.
- People, places, objects, and events can all be compared and contrasted.

Read this short history of blue jeans. As you read, think about the ways that the first jeans and modern jeans are alike and the ways that they are different.

During the California Gold Rush of 1849, miners noticed that their pants wore out quickly as they dug for gold. A young immigrant named Levi Strauss sold the miners a strong blue cotton cloth. It was known as denim. Miners asked for the denim cloth to be made into work pants. The pants were sewn together and made stronger by adding rivets to the pocket corners. Before long, all the gold miners were wearing these tough but comfortable pants. They were the first blue jeans.

Modern jeans are still made of blue denim. However, they come in many other colors and styles. Also, these popular pants are no longer just worn for work. People also wear them for school, for play, and just to look stylish.

Ways in which the first jeans and modern jeans are alike:

Both are made of denim.
Both are worn for work.

Ways in which the first jeans and modern jeans are different:

The first jeans came in one color and style, but modern jeans come in many colors and styles.

The first jeans were just work clothes, but modern jeans are also worn for school, for play, and to look stylish.

Read this article about baseball in Japan. As you read, look for clue words that tell how Japanese baseball is like American baseball and how it is different. Then answer the questions.

Play Ball!

People say that baseball is "as American as apple pie." The people of Japan may not agree. They love the sport, too. Millions of Japanese fans attend baseball games or watch them on TV.

Like the United States, Japan has two major leagues. Every fall, the best team from each league competes in the Japan Series. The Japan Series is similar to America's World Series.

There are also differences between Japanese baseball and American baseball. Baseball fields in Japan are smaller than those in the United States. In Japan, each major league has only 6 teams. The major leagues in the United States have about 15 teams each. Japanese teams also play fewer games each season than American teams.

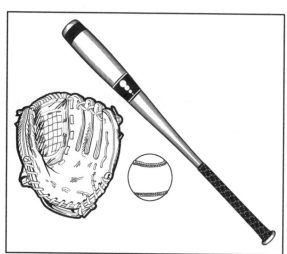

1. How are baseball teams in Japan and in the United States alike?

   Ⓐ Both compete in the Japan Series.

   Ⓑ Both have two major leagues.

   Ⓒ Both play the same number of games each season.

   Ⓓ Both play on small fields.

2. Which clue word in the article signals that the Japan Series and America's World Series are alike?

   Ⓐ different

   Ⓑ same

   Ⓒ similar

   Ⓓ like

Work with a Partner

- Talk about your answers to the questions.
- Tell why you chose your answers.
- Then talk about what you have learned so far about comparing and contrasting.

> **REVIEW**
>
> Comparing is finding ways that things are alike.
> Contrasting is finding ways that things are different.
>
> - Look for clue words that signal a likeness, or a comparison, such as *both*, *same*, *like*, *alike*, and *similar*.
> - Look for clue words that signal a difference, or a contrast, such as *but*, *unlike*, *different*, *however*, and *whereas*.
> - Look for people, places, objects, and events that are being compared and contrasted.

Read this article about crocodiles and alligators. As you read, ask yourself, "How are these animals alike? How are they different?" Then answer the questions.

Reptile Relatives

Most people can't tell the difference between an alligator and a crocodile. That's not surprising. These large reptiles look a lot alike. Both have four short legs and a long, powerful tail. Their skin is greenish brown and covered with scales. Also, their eyes and nostrils are on top of their head.

There are many ways to tell the two reptiles apart. An alligator has a broad head and a rounded snout. A crocodile has a narrow head and a long, pointed snout. When an alligator's jaws are closed, its lower teeth are hidden. But when a crocodile's jaws are shut, a tooth sticks out on each side.

Both reptiles must live in warm waters to survive. Alligators like only fresh water. Crocodiles, however, sometimes swim out to sea for a short time. Alligators are found in only two places. They live in parts of China and in the southeastern United States. Crocodiles, however, live in many places. They are found in South America, Central America, Africa, Asia, and Australia. A few are also found in southern Florida, with their alligator cousins.

alligator

3. In what way are alligators and crocodiles alike?
   - Ⓐ Their lower teeth don't show when their jaws are shut.
   - Ⓑ They both have narrow heads.
   - Ⓒ Their eyes and nostrils are on top of their head.
   - Ⓓ They both live only in fresh water.

4. Which clue word in the article signals how the places in which crocodiles live are different from the places in which alligators live?
   - Ⓐ both
   - Ⓑ but
   - Ⓒ different
   - Ⓓ however

Which Answer Is Correct and Why?

Look at the answer choices for each question.
Read why each answer choice is correct or not correct.

3. In what way are alligators and crocodiles alike?

   Ⓐ **Their lower teeth don't show when their jaws are shut.**

   This answer is not correct because the article states that an alligator's lower teeth are hidden when its jaws are closed. When a crocodile's jaws are shut, a tooth on each side sticks out.

   Ⓑ **They both have narrow heads.**

   This answer is not correct because only crocodiles have a narrow head. Alligators have a broad, rounded head.

   ⬤ **Their eyes and nostrils are on top of their head.**

   This answer is correct because this is a comparison that is stated in the first paragraph.

   Ⓓ **They both live only in fresh water.**

   This answer is not correct because while alligators do live only in fresh water, crocodiles can also live in the sea for a short time.

4. Which clue word in the article signals how the places in which crocodiles live are different from the places in which alligators live?

   Ⓐ **both**

   This answer is not correct because the word *both* is usually used to compare things, not contrast them.

   Ⓑ **but**

   This answer is not correct because the word *but* is not used in the paragraph that describes the places where the reptiles live.

   Ⓒ **different**

   This answer is not correct because the word *different* is not used in the article.

   ⬤ **however**

   This answer is correct because a contrast between where crocodiles and alligators live is in the last paragraph. The paragraph states, *"Alligators are found in only two places. . . . Crocodiles, however, live in many places."*

MORE TO KNOW	Sometimes, there are no clue words in a reading passage to signal that things are being compared or contrasted. When there are no clue words, • think about the people, places, objects, or events that you read about. Ask yourself, "How are they alike? How are they different?" • think about the people, places, objects, or events that you read about. Ask yourself, "What things are compared or contrasted? In what ways are they compared? In what ways are they contrasted?"

Read this article written by Adina. Then answer the questions.

Best Friends

My best friend, Rajini, and I have a lot in common. We were both born on June 24 in India. I was born in the old city of Delhi. Rajini was born in New Delhi, the capital. Our families moved to the United States when Rajini and I were two years old.

Rajini and I are in the fourth grade at the Estabrook School. She has Mr. Saxon. I have Ms. Ortega. After school, we take dance lessons together. We also have the same piano teacher. I study classical piano. Rajini studies jazz.

At home, I have two older brothers. Rajini has a younger sister. Our fathers are both engineers. My mother is an architect, whereas Rajini's mother is a writer. Our families live in the same apartment building. We're not allowed to have dogs or cats in our building. Rajini, though, does have a goldfish.

Some people think Rajini and I are sisters. We're both tall and thin and have short black hair. Only I, however, wear glasses. If I take them off, it's hard to tell us apart.

5. How is Rajini like Adina?
  Ⓐ She was also born in Delhi, India.
  Ⓑ Her birthday is also June 24.
  Ⓒ She also likes jazz.
  Ⓓ She also wears glasses.

6. In what way are the girls different?
  Ⓐ Adina has two older brothers, and Rajini has an older sister.
  Ⓑ Adina's mother is an architect, and Rajini's mother is an engineer.
  Ⓒ Adina does not have a pet, but Rajini does.
  Ⓓ Adina lives in the city, but Rajini lives in a small town.

7. Which of these tells one thing the girls have in common?
  Ⓐ Both are in fourth grade.
  Ⓑ Both attend Brook School.
  Ⓒ Both have the same classroom teacher.
  Ⓓ Both study classical piano.

8. Adina compared her looks to Rajini's by saying that
  Ⓐ no one can ever tell them apart.
  Ⓑ both of them are short and thin.
  Ⓒ both of them have brown hair.
  Ⓓ people think they are sisters.

Read this chart, which describes some of the ways that frogs and toads are alike and ways that they are different. Then answer the questions.

Quality	Frogs	Toads
Can survive only in moist conditions	✓	✓
Live mostly in water	✓	
Live mostly on land		✓
Are cold-blooded animals	✓	✓
Lay their eggs in the water	✓	✓
Begin life as tadpoles with gills and tails	✓	✓
Adults have lungs instead of gills	✓	✓
Adults have no tail	✓	✓
Use long, sticky tongue to catch insects	✓	✓
Feed mostly on insects	✓	✓
Have moist, smooth skin	✓	
Have dry, bumpy skin		✓
Have long, powerful back legs for leaping	✓	
Have shorter legs		✓
Are excellent jumpers	✓	
Do more hopping than jumping		✓
Color usually matches their surroundings	✓	✓

frog

toad

9. Which of these tells one way that frogs and toads are different?
   - Ⓐ Only frogs lay their eggs in the water.
   - Ⓑ Toads' color matches their surroundings.
   - Ⓒ Only frogs do more hopping than jumping.
   - Ⓓ Frogs live mostly in water.

10. One way that frogs and toads are alike is that
    - Ⓐ they have long, powerful back legs.
    - Ⓑ they use their tongues to catch insects.
    - Ⓒ they have moist skin.
    - Ⓓ they live mostly on land.

11. Which three qualities do frogs have in common with toads?
    - Ⓐ are cold-blooded, have bumpy skin, color matches their surroundings
    - Ⓑ lay their eggs in the water, are excellent jumpers, live mostly in water
    - Ⓒ adults have lungs, eat insects, can survive only in moist conditions
    - Ⓓ begin life as tadpoles, adults have no tail, have dry skin

12. Which of these is true?
    - Ⓐ Frogs and toads are alike in more ways than they are different.
    - Ⓑ Frogs and toads are different in more ways than they are alike.
    - Ⓒ Toads can do everything that frogs can do and more.
    - Ⓓ Frogs are just like toads, except that frogs live mostly in water.

> **TEST TIPS**
>
> - A test question about comparing and contrasting may ask you how things are alike or how they are different.
> - A test question about comparing and contrasting may contain a clue word. Words such as *same*, *like*, *alike*, and *similar* signal that you are to compare things. Words such as *different*, *unlike*, or *not like* signal that you are to contrast things.

Read this article about something that seems unlikely, but is true. Then answer questions about the article. Choose the best answer for Numbers 13 and 14.

Unlikely Likenesses

In 1860, Abraham Lincoln became president of the United States. The secretary who helped him with his work was a man. His last name was Kennedy. One Friday, in 1865, the president and his wife went to a play at Ford's Theater in Washington, D.C. During the play, John Wilkes Booth shot the president in the back of the head. Booth then ran to a warehouse to hide. Lincoln died the next morning. Andrew Johnson, his vice president, became the new president. Johnson was born in 1808.

In 1960, John F. Kennedy was elected president. His secretary was Evelyn Lincoln. One Friday, in 1963, the president and his wife were riding through Dallas, Texas. Suddenly, bullets struck the back of the president's head. A man named Lee Harvey Oswald fired the shots from a warehouse. He ran to a theater to hide. Kennedy died within the hour. His vice president, Lyndon Johnson, took over as president. Johnson was born in 1908.

13. What is similar about the lives of John F. Kennedy and Abraham Lincoln?

- Ⓐ Both men had a vice president named Johnson.
- Ⓑ Both men died on a Friday.
- Ⓒ Both men were born in a year ending with the numbers 08.
- Ⓓ Both men had secretaries named Lincoln.

14. The stories of John Wilkes Booth and Lee Harvey Oswald are different because

- Ⓐ Booth shot a president on a Friday, but Oswald did not.
- Ⓑ Booth ran to a warehouse, but Oswald did not.
- Ⓒ Oswald shot a president from behind, but Booth did not.
- Ⓓ Oswald did not mean to shoot the president, but Booth did.

Read this friendly letter about family vacation plans. Then answer questions about the letter. Choose the best answer for Numbers 15 and 16.

May 7, 2009

Dear Greg,

Our family is trying to decide where we will spend our vacation this year. My dad wants to go camping, but my mom wants to visit New York City. I'm not sure where I want to go yet.

Camping in the woods will be peaceful. There will be lots of open space, fresh air, and the smell of pine around us. We can hike in the woods, swim in the pond, and play games all day. We'll fall asleep to the chirping of crickets and wake to the chirping of birds. Then again, if we go camping, we may struggle with bugs and bad weather. Nothing is worse than getting lots of mosquito bites! Besides, if it rains, there'll be nothing to do.

If we go to New York, we can see skyscrapers, stroll through Central Park, or ride the ferry to the Statue of Liberty. If it rains, we can visit the Empire State Building, the Museum of Natural History, or the United Nations. We can also go shopping or swim in the hotel's indoor pool.

New York City, of course, will be crowded and noisy. We'll breathe in car exhaust and other polluted air. Besides, spending time in the city can be expensive. We'll have to rent a hotel room, eat at restaurants, and park our car in a garage.

At the end of this month, we're going to vote on where we're going. Please write with suggestions that will help me make my choice.

Your friend,
Darrius

15. How are a camping trip and a visit to New York City alike?
    Ⓐ Both trips cost about the same amount of money.
    Ⓑ Both trips offer a lot to see and do.
    Ⓒ Both trips are peaceful.
    Ⓓ Both trips offer plenty of ways to get fresh air.

16. What is one way that a camping trip and a visit to New York City are different?
    Ⓐ There's no place to swim in the city.
    Ⓑ There's less chance of bad weather in the city.
    Ⓒ On a camping trip, it's easier to fall asleep.
    Ⓓ There's less open space and more noise in the city.

What Is a Prediction?

A prediction is a good guess about something that will happen at a later time.
A prediction is often based on information you already know or have read about.

1 Write one thing you guessed would happen yesterday or the day before.

_____

_____

2 Write the clues that made you guess this would happen.

_____

_____

_____

3 Was your guess correct? Why do you think this was so?

_____

_____

Work with a Partner

- Tell each other something you thought would happen that actually did happen. You might tell about a surprise quiz you thought a teacher was going to give or news you thought a friend might tell you.

- Take turns explaining why you thought your predictions would happen.

- Make predictions about events and characters
  (GPI.R.2)

58

How Do You Make a Prediction?

You can make a prediction about a reading passage before you begin reading. Sometimes the title of the passage gives you a clue about what you will read.

Read the title of this passage. Then read the passage. See if you can figure out what will probably happen next.

Lonely Legs

Legs the Spider was unhappy. He didn't feel like weaving a new web, and he didn't feel like going for a walk. Legs just wanted someone to be friends with. But he was new to the woods, and he didn't know anyone. Legs watched a family of spiders walking down to the pond for a picnic. He saw that one of the spiders was about his age. Legs had an idea.

---

1. Think about the title of the passage. You can figure out from the title how the character Legs is feeling.

2. Now let's think about what you read in the passage.

   Look at the magnifying glass below. It shows the last sentence of the passage. See if you can make a prediction about what might happen next in the story.

Legs had an idea.

Predictions:

1. Legs will go to the pond.

2. Legs will follow the family of spiders.

3. Look at the box next to the magnifying glass.
   The box shows two predictions about what might happen next.
   The two predictions are almost alike. Either one is correct, based on the story.

4. Reread the title and the information in the passage.
   How do you think the story will probably end?

5. Write your prediction on the lines below.

_____

_____

WHAT TO KNOW	When you think about what might happen next in a reading passage, you are **making a prediction**. Making a prediction is a way of using clues from a reading passage, as well as things you already know, to make a good guess about what might happen next. • Clues are often in the title of a reading passage. Read the title, and then make a prediction about what you will be reading. • Clues are often in the details of a reading passage. Details about the things characters do and say often help you make a prediction about what they might do or say later in the story. • Clues are often in the pictures included with a passage. Pictures often show something that is happening or will happen soon.

Read this story about Janelle. As you read, think about what might happen next in the story.

First Day at Camp

It was Janelle's first day at sleepover camp. She was sitting on her cot, waiting for her cabinmates to arrive. Janelle was looking forward to camp. She liked sports, crafts, and the outdoors. Still, she was nervous. She didn't know anyone and worried that she wouldn't make any friends. What if her cabinmates didn't like her? Just then, Janelle heard giggling and laughter outside. A girl called out, "Janelle, are you in there? We want to meet our new cabinmate!"

Think about what you read and what you already know about meeting new people. Make a good guess about what might happen next. Then continue reading to see how close your guess is to what actually happens.

Suddenly, three girls burst into the cabin. The girls introduced themselves to Janelle. They talked excitedly about the weeks ahead. Janelle breathed a sigh of relief. She knew that she would have a lot of fun with her new friends.

What happened next in the story was:

Janelle meets her new cabinmates and is relieved to find they are friendly.

Read this story about an Irish couple. As you read, ask yourself, "What does the title tell me about what I will be reading? Which details will help me predict what will happen next?" Then answer the questions.

A Fisherman's Sweater

Long ago on the green island of Ireland, a woman named Nancy lived with her husband, Ian. They lived by the blue Atlantic in a cozy stone cottage with a thatched roof. Six days a week, Ian rowed his fishing boat out to sea. Nancy stayed at home doing chores. When she had time, she knitted sweaters for Ian. Each sweater had a bold pattern.

One stormy day, Ian did not return as usual. Nancy watched for him at the cottage window. She was afraid that Ian had drowned.

At last, she saw someone in the distance. A man was walking toward the cottage. Nancy strained her eyes to see who it was. The man wore a sweater. Nancy recognized the pattern immediately.

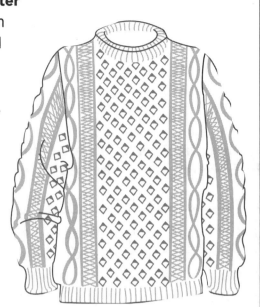

1. What do you think would most likely happen next in the story?
   Ⓐ Nancy will see Ian's face and run outside to greet him.
   Ⓑ A fisherman will bring news that Ian has drowned.
   Ⓒ A stranger will ask for shelter from the storm.
   Ⓓ A friend who has a sweater similar to Ian's will visit Nancy.

2. Where did you find the best clue to help you make your prediction?
   Ⓐ in the title of the story
   Ⓑ in the picture that was included with the story
   Ⓒ in the details about Ian's job
   Ⓓ in the details about the sweaters that Nancy knitted

Work with a Partner

- Talk about your answers to the questions.
- Tell why you chose your answers.
- Then talk about what you have learned so far about making predictions.

REVIEW	Making a prediction is a way of using clues from a reading passage, as well as things you already know, to make a good guess about what might happen next.

- Look for clues in a reading passage to help you predict what might happen next. Clues are often in the title, in the details, and in any pictures.

- Ask yourself, "What do I already know about the things I am reading about?"

Read this Greek myth about Achilles. As you read, look for clues that will help you predict the ending of the myth. Then answer the questions.

Achilles was a famous Greek warrior during the Trojan War. He was the son of the sea goddess Thetis. When Achilles was an infant, Thetis dipped him into the magical waters of the River Styx. Thus, every part of Achilles' body was protected from harm, except for one spot. This weak spot was the heel by which Thetis had held him.

When Achilles was young, he had to make a difficult choice. He could choose either a long and ordinary life, or a short, but heroic, one. Achilles chose the second.

Achilles grew up to be a brave warrior and a loyal friend. But he was also famous for his bad moods. In one battle, Achilles got into an argument. He stomped off the battlefield. While he was gone, his best friend, Patroclus, was killed by the Trojan hero Hector. Achilles was filled with guilt and rage. He killed Hector. Hector's brother, Paris, heard about the death and immediately sought revenge.

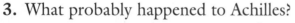

3. What probably happened to Achilles?
   Ⓐ He remained safe from harm because Thetis protected him.
   Ⓑ He killed Paris the next time they were in battle.
   Ⓒ Paris killed him by wounding him in the heel.
   Ⓓ He refused to fight ever again so that he could live a long life.

4. How might things have been different if Achilles had not left the battlefield?
   Ⓐ Achilles might still be living today.
   Ⓑ Patroclus might not have died.
   Ⓒ Patroclus probably would have killed Hector.
   Ⓓ Paris would have become Achilles' friend.

Which Answer Is Correct and Why?

Look at the answer choices for each question.
Read why each answer choice is correct or not correct.

3. **What probably happened to Achilles?**

   Ⓐ **He remained safe from harm because Thetis protected him.**

   This answer is not correct because clues in the myth suggest that Achilles' life was in danger despite his mother's protection. He not only had a weak spot on his heel, but he also had chosen a short, but heroic, life.

   Ⓑ **He killed Paris the next time they were in battle.**

   This answer is not correct because, although both men were enemies, it was more likely that Paris would have killed Achilles. Achilles had already sought his revenge for the death of Patroclus by killing Hector. Paris was still seeking revenge against Achilles for killing his brother.

   ● **Paris killed him by wounding him in the heel.**

   This answer is correct because Paris sought revenge for his brother's death, and Achilles' only weak spot was his heel.

   Ⓓ **He refused to fight ever again so that he could live a long life.**

   This answer is not correct because the myth states that Achilles chose to live a short, but heroic, life. And since Achilles was famous for his bravery and determination, he was not likely to stop fighting.

4. **How might things have been different if Achilles had not left the battlefield?**

   Ⓐ **Achilles might still be living today.**

   This answer is not correct because the myth states that Achilles had chosen a short, but heroic, life. Also, the weak spot on his heel would have prevented him from living forever.

   ● **Patroclus might not have died.**

   This answer is correct because if Achilles had been present on the battlefield, Hector might not have killed Patroclus. The myth states that Achilles was *"a brave warrior and a loyal friend."* This clue suggests that Achilles would have fought courageously to protect his friend's life.

   Ⓒ **Patroclus probably would have killed Hector.**

   This answer is not correct because there are no clues to suggest that Patroclus would have killed Hector if Achilles had stayed on the battlefield.

   Ⓓ **Paris would have become Achilles' friend.**

   This answer is not correct because Paris was a Trojan. He was one of the enemies whom Achilles was fighting against. The two men were unlikely to become friends.

MORE TO KNOW	• Look for clues in the reading passage that tell what the characters are like. Think about how the characters behave, how they are feeling, and the things they say and do. • Link the clues with what you know from your own experiences. Ask yourself, "What have people like this character done in a similar situation?"

Read this legend about Robin Hood. Then answer the questions.

   Long ago in England, there was a bold outlaw named Robin Hood. He lived in Sherwood Forest with his band of merry men. Robin Hood was considered a hero by many. He stole from the rich and gave what he stole to the poor.

   King Henry of England ordered the sheriff of Nottingham to arrest Robin Hood. The sheriff tried to think of a trick to draw Robin Hood out of hiding. He knew that Robin Hood was quite skilled with his bow and arrow. So the sheriff decided to have an archery contest. The grand prize would be an arrow made of pure gold.

   When Robin Hood heard about the contest, he made plans to go. His merry men warned him that the sheriff was laying a trap, but Robin Hood was not afraid. On the day of the contest, he disguised himself as a beggar. No one recognized the stranger.

   The beggar ended up being one of the three best archers. On the archers' last turn, only the beggar's arrow landed in the very center of the target. With much fuss, the sheriff congratulated the winner. He then handed the beggar the golden arrow.

5. What do you think the beggar did next?
   Ⓐ He refused the prize he was given.
   Ⓑ He accused the sheriff of being a fool.
   Ⓒ He accepted the prize and quickly left.
   Ⓓ He revealed who he really was.

6. Which clue first hints that Robin Hood might win the contest?
   Ⓐ Robin Hood was a bold outlaw.
   Ⓑ Robin Hood was quite skilled with his bow and arrow.
   Ⓒ Robin Hood was not afraid of the sheriff.
   Ⓓ No one recognized Robin Hood in his disguise.

7. If the sheriff later called Robin Hood a coward for not participating in the contest, Robin Hood would probably
   Ⓐ demand an apology.
   Ⓑ send the sheriff a message saying who really won the prize.
   Ⓒ tell the sheriff that he disagreed with him.
   Ⓓ ignore the insult because of his fear of the sheriff.

8. If the sheriff later discovered who the beggar was, he would most likely
   Ⓐ be furious that he had been tricked.
   Ⓑ accept that Robin Hood had won fairly.
   Ⓒ confess his mistake to the king.
   Ⓓ admit that Robin Hood was very clever.

Read this book review by a fourth-grade student. Then answer the questions.

Margaret Bourke-White: Photographer

Catherine A. Welch wrote the biography *Margaret Bourke-White*. It tells about the life of this brave photographer.

The author begins with the photographer's early life. Margaret was born in 1906 in New York City. Young Margaret always liked adventure. Yet, she was afraid of many things. Her parents helped her to face her fears.

Margaret began taking photos in college to earn money. She often took great risks to get her pictures. She enjoyed doing these daring things. "The camera was her ticket to adventure," explains the author.

Margaret traveled all over the world. She became well known for her pictures of people facing difficult situations. Much of her work appeared in *Life* magazine. During World War II, Margaret photographed soldiers. Her pictures showed the soldiers on the battlefield, in the air, and at sea. Nothing stopped her from getting the pictures she wanted.

When the war ended, Margaret took pictures of the German death camps. Millions of Jewish people had been killed there. These photographs were probably the most difficult ones Margaret had ever taken.

9. Predict what might have happened if Margaret had not been willing to take risks.
   - (A) Her parents would have been angry with her.
   - (B) She would not have become well known.
   - (C) She would not have become a photographer.
   - (D) She would not have finished college.

10. During World War II, a torpedo struck a ship that Margaret was traveling on. What do you think she did next?
   - (A) She ran toward the lifeboats immediately.
   - (B) She kept snapping pictures until the last possible moment.
   - (C) She was so afraid that she couldn't do anything.
   - (D) She stopped working for *Life* magazine.

11. Predict how people reacted to Margaret's photographs of the death camps.
   - (A) They were shocked by what her pictures revealed.
   - (B) They were angry at her for showing them the truth.
   - (C) They demanded that she stop taking such horrible pictures.
   - (D) They told her that a woman didn't belong in the camps.

12. What will the book reviewer most likely write about in the next paragraph?
   - (A) additional biographies by Catherine A. Welch
   - (B) other women photographers
   - (C) Margaret's life until her death
   - (D) life in Germany after the war

TEST TIPS

- A test question about making a prediction may ask you to make a good guess about what will happen next in a reading passage or what might happen in the future.

- A test question about making a prediction usually contains the words *predict, probably,* or *most likely.*

Read this newspaper article about a peculiar event. Then answer questions about the article. Choose the best answer for Numbers 13 and 14.

The Daily Galaxy   Special Edition   July 19, 1963

SUTTON, NH—A couple from Sutton, New Hampshire, claim that they were kidnapped by aliens last week. Martin and Roz Well were driving home around midnight on Wednesday. Suddenly, they were blinded by a strong white light. They stopped their car and got out. In the sky overhead, they saw a saucer-shaped object. Seconds later, the Wells were sucked up into the "flying saucer." The next thing they knew, they were surrounded by aliens. The Wells described them as small gray creatures. They had egg-shaped heads and big, dark eyes.

The Wells can't remember anything else about being on board the spaceship. After what seemed like only a few minutes, they were allowed to go. However, they later learned that they had been gone for five days.

Every year, hundreds of people report seeing strange objects in the sky. Most sightings turn out to be ordinary aircraft or weather balloons. Or they might be natural wonders, such as clouds or shooting stars. Stories about visitors from outer space usually prove false. So far, police have been unable to find any proof of a spacecraft near Sutton.

---

13. Predict how people will most likely react to the Wells' story.

    Ⓐ Most people will say the story is true.

    Ⓑ Most people will say the story is made up.

    Ⓒ Most people will claim that they were also kidnapped by aliens.

    Ⓓ Most people will be afraid to leave their homes at night.

14. Which of these would most likely happen if someone provided proof that a flying saucer appeared near Sutton?

    Ⓐ Police would insist that no proof could possibly exist.

    Ⓑ No one would search for additional proof.

    Ⓒ Astronauts would search for the object in space.

    Ⓓ The Wells would be asked more questions about their experience.

Read this story about a boy's first experience on ice skates. Then answer questions about the story. Choose the best answer for Numbers 15 and 16

Roberto was usually a confident kid. He was good at most things he did. Right at this moment, though, Roberto wasn't feeling so sure about himself. Today was the day he had agreed to go ice-skating with his best friend, David.

Until last year, Roberto lived in Florida. The weather there is too warm to freeze lakes and ponds, and few towns had indoor rinks. So the only skating Roberto ever did was on in-line skates. He loved the feeling of speeding across the pavement. He was fast but always in control. He hoped that his skill on ice skates would prove to be as good as his skill on in-line skates.

Roberto and David walked in the crisp, cold air to the local indoor rink. Roberto sighed deeply before opening the door. The moment of truth was finally here. Would he leave as a proud skater or as an embarrassed failure? David promised Roberto that he'd be with him every step, or slip, of the way.

Roberto laced up his skates and wobbled over to the edge of the rink. He took a deep breath and stepped onto the ice. Roberto stood there for a while, holding onto the boards. Finally, he gathered up his courage and took a step forward. Then another. And another. He decided he was ready to try gliding forward on one foot. Roberto took off, lost his footing, and fell hard! David grabbed him under the arms and picked him up. Roberto tried again. He fell again. And again. And again! But Roberto was determined to do better, so he kept on trying.

15. What will Roberto most likely do next?
  Ⓐ He will give up and take off his skates.
  Ⓑ He will skate longer without falling.
  Ⓒ He will ask David to stop helping him.
  Ⓓ He will sit on the ice and refuse to get up.

16. Predict what will probably happen if Roberto goes ice-skating again.
  Ⓐ He'll refuse to go with David.
  Ⓑ He'll watch everyone else skate.
  Ⓒ He'll enjoy skating and do well.
  Ⓓ He'll wish he'd never agreed to skate.

Read this folktale from Africa. Then answer questions about the folktale. Choose the best answer for Numbers 1 through 6.

An old man had three sons. When they had grown into manhood, he called them together. He ordered them to go out and bring him food and clothing since he was no longer able to provide for himself.

The three brothers set out. After a very long while, they came to a large river. They decided to cross the river and then each go their separate ways. In a year's time, they would all meet at the same spot.

So, the brothers parted. At the end of the year, they found their way back to the riverside. The oldest brother asked the youngest brother what he had found during his travels. The boy replied, "I have a mirror. If you look into it, you can see all over the country."

When the second brother was asked what he had found, he replied, "I have a pair of sandals. If one puts them on, one can walk to any place in the country in one step."

Then the oldest brother said, "I have a small bag of medicine, that is all. But let us look into the mirror and see how our father is."

The three brothers looked into the mirror and saw that their father was dead. The oldest brother said, "Let us hurry home and see what we can do."

So the second brother brought out his sandals, and all three placed their feet inside them. Immediately, they raced to their father's grave. Then the oldest brother shook the medicine out of its bag and poured it over the grave.

At once their father stood before them. It was as if nothing had ever been the matter with him.

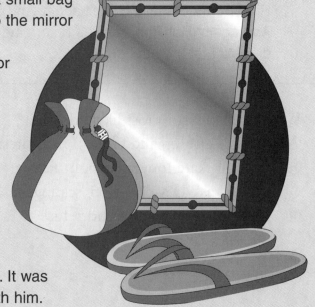

Recognizing Cause and Effect

1. Which clue word in the folktale signals the reason why the old man sent his sons away?
   - (A) if
   - (B) so
   - (C) since
   - (D) because

Comparing and Contrasting

4. How was the medicine bag different from the sandals?
   - (A) Only the sandals had special power.
   - (B) Only the medicine bag could bring the father back to life.
   - (C) Only the younger brother could use the medicine bag.
   - (D) Only the medicine bag was found during the brothers' travels.

Recognizing Cause and Effect

2. What happened when the three brothers looked into the mirror?
   - (A) They raced to their father's grave.
   - (B) They saw that their father was old and frail.
   - (C) They returned to the riverside.
   - (D) They saw that their father was no longer alive.

Making Predictions

5. What would most likely happen next?
   - (A) The father will ask his sons to show him what they found on their journey.
   - (B) The father will tell the sons that he needs a new pair of sandals.
   - (C) The sons will leave once more in search of other unusual objects.
   - (D) The sons will beg their father's forgiveness for being away so long.

Comparing and Contrasting

3. How were the oldest brother and the youngest brother alike?
   - (A) Both cared about their father.
   - (B) Both found their treasure in the same spot.
   - (C) Both liked practicing magic tricks.
   - (D) Both knew a lot about medicine.

Making Predictions

6. If the father sent his sons off for food and clothing once more, they would probably
   - (A) demand that their father take care of himself.
   - (B) return to the same spot at the large river.
   - (C) spend a year searching for food and clothing.
   - (D) use the special mirror and sandals during their search.

Read this article about tasty inventions. Then answer questions about the article. Choose the best answer for Numbers 7 through 12.

Tasty Mistakes

Think about some of today's inventions. Most of them were the result of many years of hard work and sleepless nights. Some, however, were the result of accidents. Many of these accidents led to delicious results.

The invention of potato chips is one example of a tasty mistake. One day in 1853, there was an unhappy diner at a restaurant in Saratoga Springs, New York. He kept sending his fried potatoes back to the kitchen. He demanded that they be cut thinner and fried longer. The cook, George Crum, became annoyed with the diner. Angrily, he sliced the potatoes very, very thin. Then he fried them until they were curly crisps. Last, he salted them. To Crum's surprise, the diner ate all of the crispy, salted potatoes. He even asked for more. Today, these thin, crispy potatoes are called potato chips. They are also the most popular snack food in the United States.

Until the 1904 World's Fair in St. Louis, ice cream was always served in dishes. One hot day, a man selling ice cream at the fair ran out of bowls. The man next to him was selling waffles. The waffle seller quickly rolled up one of the thin waffles into a cone shape. Then he filled it with a scoop of ice cream. The ice-cream seller continued to sell ice cream in these new holders. Today this treat is known as the ice-cream cone.

An 11-year-old boy from California accidentally invented another cold treat. One night in 1905, Frank Epperson mixed up a drink. It was made with sugared powder and soda water. Then he left the drink on his back porch. The stirring stick was still in it. The temperature dropped overnight, and the mixture froze. The next morning, the boy found a stick of frozen soda water instead of his drink. Eighteen years later, Frank started a business that produced iced pops on a stick. These frozen treats were sold in seven fruit flavors. In time, they came to be called Popsicles®.

Recognizing Cause and Effect

7. The potato chip was invented because
   Ⓐ a chef wanted to create a new food using potatoes.
   Ⓑ a waiter accidentally cut some potatoes too thin.
   Ⓒ a customer liked to eat crispy foods.
   Ⓓ a cook was annoyed with a diner's complaints.

Recognizing Cause and Effect

8. An ice-cream seller at the 1904 World's Fair ran out of bowls, so he
   Ⓐ asked the waffle seller what to do.
   Ⓑ served the ice cream in cone-shaped waffles.
   Ⓒ stopped selling ice cream.
   Ⓓ served the ice cream in paper cups.

Comparing and Contrasting

9. In what way is a Popsicle® different from an ice-cream cone?
   Ⓐ A Popsicle is more popular on a hot day.
   Ⓑ The Popsicle was invented before the ice-cream cone.
   Ⓒ A Popsicle is a hand-held treat.
   Ⓓ A Popsicle is made of frozen soda water, not frozen cream.

Comparing and Contrasting

10. How were Frank Epperson and George Crum alike?
    Ⓐ Both invented a frozen treat.
    Ⓑ Both created a popular snack.
    Ⓒ Both lived in California.
    Ⓓ Both planned to be inventors.

Making Predictions

11. How would visitors to the 1904 World's Fair probably have reacted to the first ice-cream cones?
    Ⓐ They would have demanded that their ice cream be served in bowls.
    Ⓑ They would have said that they'd rather have a Popsicle.
    Ⓒ They would have never eaten ice cream in a dish again.
    Ⓓ They would have been excited to have tried this new, tasty treat.

Making Predictions

12. Earmuffs were invented in 1873 by a young boy from Maine. Predict which of these most likely led to the invention.
    Ⓐ The boy was afraid of loud noises.
    Ⓑ The boy was tired of having cold ears every time he went skating.
    Ⓒ The boy was entering a contest for young inventors.
    Ⓓ The boy was annoyed by the sounds of life in a busy city.

What Is Word Meaning in Context?

Sometimes when you speak with someone, you hear a word you've never heard before. Many times you can figure out the meaning of the word by how the person uses it.

1 Write what you think the word *quench* means. It's okay if you don't know the real meaning. Just make a good guess.

_____

2 Someone says to you: "<u>A cold glass of water will quench my thirst.</u>" Write what you think the word *quench* means now.

_____

3 Write the clues in the underlined sentence that helped you figure out what the word *quench* means.

_____

_____

_____

Work with a Partner

- Talk about some of the new words you have learned lately.
- Take turns using each new word in a sentence. Make sure your sentence gives a good hint about the meaning of the word.
- Have your partner guess what the new word means.

- Use context to determine meaning (**CPI.R**)
- Determine meaning of unfamiliar words by using context clues (**CPI.R**)

How Do You Find Word Meaning in Context?

When you come to a new word in a reading passage, you can find word meaning in context. You can look for clues to help you figure out what the word means. Clues might be in the sentence where the word is found. Clues might also be in the sentence just before or just after the one in which the word is found.

Read this passage about tall tales. See if you can figure out what the word *feat* means.

> A tall tale is a kind of story in which the truth is stretched. The characters in the story do unbelievable things. Paul Bunyan is a popular hero in many tall tales. Paul Bunyan is a giant lumberjack who always performs an amazing feat in every story told about him. In one tall tale, he cuts down an entire forest in just a few hours!

1. Let's narrow down the clues to figure out what the word *feat* means.

   Look at the chart below.
   It shows three sentences: the one that comes before the word *feat*, the one that contains the word *feat*, and the one that comes after the word *feat*.

   Look carefully at the sentences that come before and after the word *feat*.

Paul Bunyan is a popular hero in many tall tales.	Paul Bunyan is a giant lumberjack who always performs an amazing feat in every story told about him.	In one tall tale, he cuts down an entire forest in just a few hours!
Before		After

2. Now think about what the clues in the sentences tell you:

   Paul Bunyan is in many tall tales, and tall tales are stories that stretch the truth.

   Paul Bunyan does something amazing in every story about him.

   Paul Bunyan can cut down an entire forest in just a few hours.

3. So the word *feat* must mean _____ .

WHAT TO KNOW

When you use clues in a reading passage to figure out the meaning of a new word, you are **finding word meaning in context**. The words and phrases around a new word often provide clues to the word's meaning. These clues are called **context clues**.

- Context clues are often in the sentence where the new word appears. They can also be in the sentences before and after the new word.

- Clues about the meaning of a new word are often found by thinking about the way the word is used in the sentence.

- Clues about the meaning of a new word can be found by thinking about the details in the paragraph where the new word is found.

Read this paragraph about Craig. As you read, think about the meaning of the word *ailing* in the second sentence.

It was supposed to be the first day of his new job, but Craig did not feel well. He had to call his boss to say that he was ailing. What a day to be ill! Craig couldn't believe his bad luck.

You can figure out the meaning of the word *ailing* by looking at the words and phrases around it. The phrase *did not feel well* and the word *ill* are clues to the meaning of the word *ailing*.

The meaning of the word *ailing* is "unwell or ill."

Read this article about diamonds. As you read, ask yourself, "What clues will I use to figure out the meaning of the word *clarity*?" Then answer the questions.

Diamonds are the world's hardest material. Most diamonds formed deep inside the earth about three billion years ago. Lava from volcanoes eventually carried the crystal stones to the earth's surface.

Diamonds are the most highly prized stone. However, they vary greatly in quality. The value of a diamond depends on its color, clarity, cut, and weight.

Most natural diamonds are colorless. Some diamonds, though, have elements that give them color. Diamonds can also be red, yellow, pink, brown, green, or blue.

A diamond's clarity is what makes it sparkle brightly or appear dull. Diamonds with good clarity are easy to see through. Diamonds with poor clarity are not easy to see through. The way a diamond is cut helps show off its brightness. The better the cut, the more it shines.

Not all diamonds are used for jewelry. Most diamonds are too small or are oddly shaped. But they are still valuable. These diamonds are used to make such products as computer chips. They are also used for cutting other strong materials, such as rock, glass, steel, and even other diamonds.

1. In paragraph 4, *clarity* probably means
   - Ⓐ "colorfulness."
   - Ⓑ "hardness."
   - Ⓒ "dullness."
   - Ⓓ "clearness."

2. Which phrase gives a clue to the meaning of *clarity*?
   - Ⓐ easy to see through
   - Ⓑ most highly prized stone
   - Ⓒ have elements that give them color
   - Ⓓ the more it shines

Work with a Partner

- Talk about your answers to the questions.
- Tell why you chose your answers.
- Then talk about what you have learned so far about finding word meaning in context.

REVIEW	The words and phrases around a new word often give clues about the word's meaning.
	• Look for context clues in the sentence where the word appears. Look also in the sentences before and after the new word.
	• Look for clues about the meaning of a new word by thinking about the way the word is used in the sentence.
	• Look for clues about the meaning of a new word by thinking about the details in the paragraph where the new word is found.

Read this ad for a whale tour. As you read, think about how you will figure out the meaning of any new words. Then answer the questions.

A Whale of a Time

Here's your opportunity to see the largest creatures on Earth!

- Spend an exciting day on board *The Beluga*.
- Watch whales living in their natural environment, and talk to experts who know about the whales and their ocean habitat.
- Listen to unique whale songs, unlike anything you've ever heard.
- View the award-winning video "The Company of Whales."
- Open your eyes and hearts to the sights and sounds of the sea.

Bring your camera and join us at Dawson's Pier for the time of your life. *The Beluga* sails daily at 8:00 A.M. and 2:00 P.M. May through September.

3. You can tell that a habitat is
   Ⓐ a ship.
   Ⓑ a home.
   Ⓒ an ocean.
   Ⓓ a kind of whale.

4. In the third bullet, what is the best meaning of the word *unique*?
   Ⓐ "common"
   Ⓑ "unpopular"
   Ⓒ "one of a kind"
   Ⓓ "pleasant sounding"

Which Answer Is Correct and Why?

Look at the answer choices for each question.
Read why each answer choice is correct or not correct.

3. **You can tell that a habitat is**

   Ⓐ **a ship.**

   This answer is not correct because when the ad talks about a habitat, there are no words or phrases that describe a ship.

   ● **a home.**

   This answer is correct because the words and phrases around the word *habitat* describe where whales live— *"living," "natural environment," "ocean."* You can figure out from these clues that a habitat is probably where a whale lives, or its home.

   Ⓒ **an ocean.**

   This answer is not correct because an ocean is a kind of habitat. A whale's habitat might be the ocean, but a bear's habitat would be on land.

   Ⓓ **a kind of whale.**

   This answer is not correct because there are no words used in the ad that describe different kinds of whales.

4. **In the third bullet, what is the best meaning of the word *unique*?**

   Ⓐ **"common"**

   This answer is not correct because no words or phrases tell that whale songs are common. In fact, the words *"unlike anything you've ever heard"* give you a clue that whale songs are anything but common.

   Ⓑ **"unpopular"**

   This answer is not correct because no words or phrases tell that whale songs are unpopular. The only words used to describe whale songs are *"unlike anything you've ever heard."* This does not tell the reader whether or not the songs are popular, only that they are unusual.

   ● **"one of a kind"**

   This answer is correct. The words *"unlike anything you've ever heard"* give a clue to the meaning of the word *unique*. You can figure out that something that is not like anything you've ever heard must be one of a kind.

   Ⓓ **"pleasant sounding"**

   This answer is not correct because no words or phrases tell what the whale songs sound like, only that they are *"unique"* or *"unlike anything you've ever heard."*

MORE TO KNOW

- Look for a synonym, or a word with a similar meaning, near a new word in a reading passage.

- Look for an antonym, or a word with an opposite meaning, near a new word in a reading passage.

- Once you think you know the meaning of a new word, read the sentence where the word appears and use the new meaning. Does the sentence still make sense in the passage? If so, you've probably figured out the new word's meaning.

Read this story about a brave lighthouse keeper. Then answer the questions.

A Beacon of Hope

Lookout Lighthouse was located on an island off the coast of Maine. The 75-foot tower had a powerful signal light at the top. The flashing light was used to guide ships and warn them of the rocky islands nearby.

Most days, calm waters surrounded the lighthouse. But June 10 was not like most days. By sunrise, black clouds had rolled in. A harsh wind began whipping up turbulent waves. By noon, a furious storm swirled around the lighthouse.

Lea, the light keeper, watched from her post. She saw a ship drifting helplessly toward a rocky island. It was the *Star Erikson*.

Quickly, Lea raced to her boat. She rowed with all of her strength through the rough waters and toward the troubled vessel. Three sailors had been knocked off the ship's deck into the choppy water. Lea pulled them, one by one, into her boat. Then she rowed back to the lighthouse, following its bright beacon. Because of Lea, none of the sailors lost their lives in the terrible storm.

5. In paragraph 2, which clue word is an antonym of *turbulent*?

Ⓐ harsh

Ⓑ calm

Ⓒ furious

Ⓓ rocky

6. In paragraph 2, which word gives a clue to the meaning of *swirled*?

Ⓐ around

Ⓑ rolled

Ⓒ surrounded

Ⓓ whipping

7. In the last paragraph, which clue word is a synonym of *choppy*?

Ⓐ strength

Ⓑ troubled

Ⓒ terrible

Ⓓ rough

8. In the last paragraph, *beacon* means

Ⓐ "a signal light."

Ⓑ "a message."

Ⓒ "a tower."

Ⓓ "a lookout post."

Read this article about space stations. Then answer the questions.

Space Stations: Past, Present, and Future

Scientists believe that huge space stations orbiting Earth will provide a safe way to search the universe. The first space station was launched in 1971 by the Soviet Union. It was called *Salyut 1*. Three cosmonauts traveled around Earth in the space station for 24 days. Sadly, the three crew members died trying to return home.

Two years later, the United States launched the *Skylab* space station. It went on three missions. A crew of three astronauts carried out each mission. The astronauts performed many important experiments on *Skylab*. Several experiments helped scientists understand how the human body acts in space.

The Russian space station *Mir* was launched in 1986. In time, the space station began to wear out. In March 2001, Russia took *Mir* out of orbit and sent it plunging to Earth.

In 1993, the United States and Russia agreed to build an International Space Station, or ISS. To prepare for the project, shuttles flew to *Mir* from 1995–1998. Crews from each country traveled into space to assemble the new station. Other nations have since joined the project. Canada, Japan, and European countries now help keep the ISS up and running. Crews from different countries man the space station. They take turns. Each crew usually stays between four and six months.

The ISS orbits about 400 km above the earth. It looks like a bright star moving from west to east. You can check the NASA website to find out when the ISS can be viewed in your city or town.

9. In the first paragraph, you can tell that the word *orbiting* means
   Ⓐ "exploring."
   Ⓑ "speeding away from."
   Ⓒ "traveling toward."
   Ⓓ "traveling around."

10. In the third paragraph, which clue words act as an antonym for *plunging*?
    Ⓐ to Earth
    Ⓑ was launched
    Ⓒ wear out
    Ⓓ space station

11. In paragraph 4, which clue word is a synonym of *assemble*?
    Ⓐ build
    Ⓑ travel
    Ⓒ agree
    Ⓓ prepare

12. In paragraph 4, the best meaning of the word *man* is
    Ⓐ "to succeed in doing something."
    Ⓑ "to orbit around Earth."
    Ⓒ "to be in charge of."
    Ⓓ "to supply with equipment."

| TEST TIPS | • A test question about finding meaning in context asks you about the meaning of a word as it is used in a reading passage. The word may or may not be familiar to you. The word might be used in a new way. |
| | • A test question about finding meaning in context usually has several answer choices. Try each answer choice in the sentence in which the word appears. Decide which answer choice makes the most sense in the reading passage. |

Read this story from Chile. Then answer questions about the story. Choose the best answer for Numbers 13 and 14.

Antonio and the Thief

One day, Antonio's mother gave him some money and sent him to town to buy flour and butter. She warned him not to lose the money.

Antonio noticed that a man was following him. Antonio suspected trouble, so he came up with a plan. He pretended to hide something under his hat.

The man—who was a thief—was intrigued by what might be under his hat and kept Antonio asking about it. Antonio told him it was a chicken and asked the man to watch it for him. Antonio left the hat on the ground, and the thief greedily looked under it. He knew he'd been tricked when all he found was a rock!

As Antonio walked on, he observed the thief trailing him. So he leaned on a boulder, pretending to hold it back. He hollered to the thief, "This rock is going to crash onto the town. Please hold it while I get some stakes."

The thief held the rock, but soon he became tired and sore. Finally, he just had to let go of the rock. When it didn't move, he was furious to realize that he'd been tricked again. In his wrath, he ran to find Antonio.

Antonio sensed the thief behind him. So he stopped to tie a rope to a locust tree. Antonio loudly gasped, "The earth is turning upside down and everything except this locust tree is going to fall off. I'm going to tie myself to this tree."

The thief didn't want to fall off the earth, so he begged Antonio to tie him first. Antonio did, and then went to buy flour and butter. On his way home, he saw the thief, who realized that he had been tricked yet again!

---

13. In paragraph 3, you can tell that *intrigued* means

   Ⓐ "amused."

   Ⓑ "attacked."

   Ⓒ "fascinated."

   Ⓓ "afraid."

14. What is the best meaning of the word *wrath*?

   Ⓐ anger

   Ⓑ surprise

   Ⓒ pain

   Ⓓ exhaustion

Read this article about Mount Everest. Then answer questions about the article. Choose the best answer for Numbers 15 and 16.

On Top of the World

All mountains must rise at least 2,000 feet above sea level. Otherwise, they are just hills. The highest mountain in the world is Mount Everest. It stands between Nepal and part of China. Mount Everest is part of the Himalayas, the world's highest mountain range.

Local people call Mount Everest Chomolungma. This name means "Goddess of the Snows." The name suits the snowy giant. Mount Everest has the highest elevation of any mountain on Earth. Its peak rises 29,108 feet (about 9 kilometers) above sea level.

People began trying to climb to the top of Mount Everest in the 1920s. In 1953, two men finally succeeded. Edmund Hillary, of New Zealand, and Tenzing Norgay, a guide from Nepal, became the first people to reach the summit. Since then, hundreds of people have done the same. At the same time, many climbers have lost their lives on route.

Mount Everest is one of the world's most difficult mountains to climb. Scaling it requires special clothing, equipment, and skill. The higher a climber climbs, the thinner the air becomes. Thin air is difficult to breathe, so climbers must breathe in bottled oxygen. Also, the slopes are covered with deep snow and thick ice. Sometimes, a large mass of snow breaks loose. It can cause an avalanche that sweeps climbers down the mountain and buries them.

Another danger for climbers is the climate on top of Mount Everest. Temperatures can drop quickly, and winds can blow at speeds of 200 miles per hour.

15. In paragraph 4, the word *scaling* means
Ⓐ "falling."
Ⓑ "climbing."
Ⓒ "reaching."
Ⓓ "breathing."

16. You can tell that an avalanche is
Ⓐ a climber who slides down a mountain slope.
Ⓑ a deep crack in the ice.
Ⓒ a mass of snow that falls down a mountainside.
Ⓓ thin air that is difficult to breathe.

Lesson 8 DRAWING CONCLUSIONS AND MAKING INFERENCES

PART ONE: Think About the Strategy

What Are Conclusions and Inferences?

There are many times each day when you figure out something on your own without being told what is happening. If you see someone crying, you know that the person is sad. If you hear someone laughing, you know that the person just heard something funny.

1 Write what you can figure out about the weather if you see people outside wearing long pants and heavy coats.

_____

_____

_____

_____

2 Write the clues that helped you figure this out.

_____

_____

_____

_____

Work with a Partner

- Take turns asking each other "What can you figure out?" questions.
- Ask questions such as, "How is a cat probably feeling if you can hear it purring?"

82

- Make inferences and draw conclusions on the basis of information from the text (**GPI.R.1**)
- Draw conclusions and make inferences about events and characters (**GPI.R.2**)

- Identify a conclusion that summarizes the main idea (**GPI.R.1**)
- Identify missing information and irrelevant information (**GPI.R.1**)
- Use evidence from stories to identify themes, actions, motivations (**GPI.R.2**)

How Do You Draw Conclusions and Make Inferences?

There are many times when you read that you draw conclusions and make inferences. Sometimes the author does not give you all the details. You need to figure out some things by yourself. An author might write about a character who is biting her fingernails. The author does not need to tell you that the character is feeling nervous. You can figure this out on your own.

Read this passage about Ruth. See what you can figure out on your own.

> Ruth checked her watch. Then she looked out the window for the third time in less than a minute. Ruth didn't notice the sound of her own foot tap-tap-tapping the wood floor.

1. Let's draw a conclusion. Think about what the author tells you. Also think about what the author just hints at.

2. Look at the chart below. The first box lists three details that the author gives in the passage.

3. The second box tells what is just hinted at in the passage. The author leaves this information out.

4. What can you figure out on your own? Fill in the missing information in the last box.

What details are given?	What information does the author leave out?	What can you figure out on your own?
Ruth is checking her watch. Ruth keeps looking out the window. Ruth doesn't even notice she's tapping her foot.	The author does not tell why Ruth is doing these things.	Ruth is doing these things because _____ _____ _____

<table>
<tr><td>

WHAT TO KNOW

</td><td>

Information is sometimes not clearly stated or explained in a reading passage. You must figure out some information on your own. Whenever you figure out something the author doesn't tell you in a reading passage, you are **drawing a conclusion** or **making an inference**.

- Pay attention to the details in a reading passage. You can use these details to figure out information that is not clearly stated or explained.

- Use the details from the reading passage and what you know from your own life to draw a conclusion or to make an inference.

</td></tr>
</table>

Read this Chinese folktale about the Moon Lady. As you read, try to figure out why the Moon Lady gave whiskers to the old woman.

Long ago in China, the Moon Lady appeared to an old woman and offered to grant her one wish. The old woman was so surprised to see the Moon Lady that she couldn't speak. Finally, the old woman moved her hand up and down over her mouth and chin. She was trying to ask the Moon Lady for a little more rice to eat. The Moon Lady looked puzzled. Yet, she promised the old woman that she would grant her wish. When the old woman looked in her bowl the next morning, it still held only a few grains of rice. But when she put her hand to her face, she found that the Moon Lady had given her whiskers!

The folktale does not tell why the Moon Lady gave whiskers to the old woman. It does, however, give you details to help you figure out why this happened.

The Moon Lady offered to grant an old woman a wish.

The old woman was so surprised that she couldn't speak.

The old woman moved her hand up and down over her mouth and chin.

The Moon Lady looked puzzled.

These details help you figure out that the Moon Lady did not understand the old woman's hand movements. The Moon Lady thought that the old woman wanted whiskers. You probably know from your own experience that it can be confusing when a person uses gestures instead of words.

Read this article about the sinking of the *Titanic*. As you read, look for details that will help you figure out who survived the sinking and why. Then answer the questions.

The *Titanic* Tragedy

It was April 10, 1912. The *Titanic* had set off on its first voyage. It was traveling from England to New York. The 2,207 passengers were filled with excitement. They were on board the finest ship in the world. They were also on the first ship to be called "unsinkable." But on the evening of April 14, something went terribly wrong. At 11:45 P.M., the *Titanic* struck an iceberg. Within two and a half hours, the ship had sunk. The lives of 1,502 people were lost.

The *Titanic* had enough lifeboats for just 1,178 people. But only about 700 people actually filled the boats. The crew had ordered that "women and children go first." This rule mostly helped passengers who were traveling in first class. Only 4 of 143 women in first class died that evening. In second class, 15 of 93 women did not make it. In third class, however, 81 of 179 women were lost. As for the children, all 29 in first and second class were saved. Only 23 out of 76 children in third class survived.

1. From the article, you can tell that the lifeboats were
   Ⓐ damaged and could not be used.
   Ⓑ not necessary on the ship.
   Ⓒ not completely filled with passengers.
   Ⓓ only for people traveling in first class.

2. What information from the article helped you answer question 1?
   Ⓐ Fewer men than women survived.
   Ⓑ There were more people in third class than in first class.
   Ⓒ There were enough lifeboats for 1,178 people, but only 700 people filled the boats.
   Ⓓ Only 4 of 143 women in first class died when the *Titanic* sunk.

Work with a Partner

- Talk about your answers to the questions.
- Tell why you chose your answers.
- Then talk about what you have learned so far about drawing conclusions and making inferences.

REVIEW

Drawing a conclusion or making an inference is a way of figuring out information that is not stated in a reading passage.

- Think about the details that are stated in a reading passage. Use these details to help you figure out information that is not explained.

- Use the details from the reading passage and what you know from your own life to draw a conclusion or to make an inference.

Read this Greek myth about a proud young woman. As you read, ask yourself, "What details are stated? What information can I figure out on my own?" Then answer the questions.

Arachne was a poor young woman from Greece. She spun the most beautiful cloth. People thought that Athena, the goddess of crafts, had taught Arachne her skill. But Arachne denied this talk. She boasted that she wove better than Athena did. She even challenged Athena to a weaving contest.

On the day of the contest, Arachne and Athena worked all day. Each woman wove many colorful cloth designs. When they had finished, Athena saw that Arachne's work really was more beautiful than her own. Athena became furious and tore up Arachne's weaving. Then she turned Arachne into a spider. Since that day, spiders have woven beautiful webs.

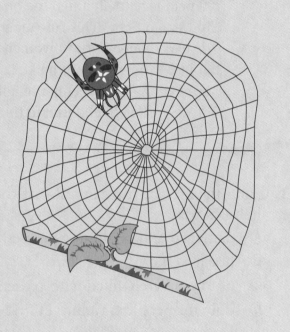

3. What can you tell about Arachne?
   - Ⓐ She was a shy woman.
   - Ⓑ She was jealous of Athena.
   - Ⓒ She was afraid of Athena.
   - Ⓓ She was proud of her skill.

4. You can conclude that Athena was
   - Ⓐ sure she would win the contest.
   - Ⓑ more powerful than Arachne.
   - Ⓒ better at other crafts than she was at weaving.
   - Ⓓ kind toward others.

Which Answer Is Correct and Why?

Look at the answer choices for each question.
Read why each answer choice is correct or not correct.

3. What can you tell about Arachne?

   Ⓐ **She was a shy woman.**

   This answer is not correct because there are no details in the myth that suggest Arachne was a shy woman. In fact, her boasting suggests the opposite is true.

   Ⓑ **She was jealous of Athena.**

   This answer is not correct because there are no details that suggest Arachne was jealous of Athena. It was Athena who was jealous of Arachne.

   Ⓒ **She was afraid of Athena.**

   This answer is not correct because there are no details that suggest Arachne was afraid of Athena. In fact, Arachne was quite bold to challenge the goddess to a weaving contest.

   ● **She was proud of her skill.**

   This answer is correct because Arachne's boasting and her challenge to Athena help you figure out that she was proud of her skill.

4. You can conclude that Athena was

   Ⓐ **sure she would win the contest.**

   This answer is not correct because there are no details in the myth that suggest Athena was certain she would win the contest. It was Arachne who was so sure.

   ● **more powerful than Arachne.**

   This answer is correct because Athena turned Arachne into a spider. You can figure out from this detail that Athena was more powerful than Arachne.

   Ⓒ **better at other crafts than she was at weaving.**

   This answer is not correct because there are no details about crafts other than weaving.

   Ⓓ **kind toward others.**

   This answer is not correct because Athena did not act kindly toward Arachne. Athena was so jealous of Arachne that she turned her into a spider.

MORE TO KNOW

- Look for details in a reading passage that tell about how a person or character looks, acts, thinks, feels, and speaks. Think about what you know about people with similar qualities.

- Look for details in a reading passage that suggest where or when something happens. If something happens at the White House, you can figure out the setting is Washington, D.C. If something happens while the stars are out, you can figure out it is nighttime.

Read this article about winter sleepers. Then answer the questions.

Many animals live in places where the winter is cold and harsh. There is not enough food to eat. Some animals survive the winter by going into a deep winter sleep. This is called hibernation.

Hibernating animals prepare for their long nap in the late summer or early fall. First, they eat lots of food. This extra food is stored in their body as fat. Then they choose a warm place to hide safely. They will stay here for several months.

When most animals hibernate, their body temperature gets very low. It lowers almost to freezing. This large drop in temperature puts the animals into a sleeplike state. It also makes their heartbeat and breathing slow down. So the animals need very little energy, and they can live off their stored fat until spring.

Some animals wake from their sleep several times during the winter. Chipmunks, for example, get up and go out when the weather is mild. They store real food instead of body fat. Bears usually sleep only through the worst weather in winter. Their body temperature drops only a few degrees. Therefore, they can easily wake up at any time.

5. You can tell from the article that when animals come out of hibernation,
   - Ⓐ their bodies stay very cold.
   - Ⓑ their body temperature rises.
   - Ⓒ they have a hard time staying awake.
   - Ⓓ they return to the north.

6. There is enough information in the article to suggest that hibernating animals
   - Ⓐ know when to sleep and when to wake.
   - Ⓑ travel south when winter comes.
   - Ⓒ always store enough food to last through the winter.
   - Ⓓ sleep underground.

7. What can you conclude about hibernating bears?
   - Ⓐ Their body temperature is always changing greatly.
   - Ⓑ Their heartbeat is quicker than that of most other hibernating animals.
   - Ⓒ They hibernate longer than most animals.
   - Ⓓ They store supplies of food in their den.

8. You can tell from the article that
   - Ⓐ few animals hibernate in winter.
   - Ⓑ hibernation is the only way for animals to survive the winter.
   - Ⓒ people also have a hard time in winter.
   - Ⓓ animals only hibernate if they live in places where winters are harsh.

Read this legend, which takes place long ago in Britain.
Then answer the questions.

The Sword and the Stone

Long ago, Uther Pendragon was the king of Britain. His chief magician was Merlin. Merlin used his powers to help the king fight his enemies and win the hand of the beautiful Igraine. When the king and queen had their first child, Merlin warned them that their son's life would be in danger at the castle. So Merlin took the baby into hiding.

Three years later, the king died. For the next twelve years, the lords and their knights fought over who should be the next king. Then one winter, Merlin came out of hiding. He told the Archbishop of Canterbury to gather all the nobles at the cathedral. When they arrived, the nobles saw that a stone had been set in the churchyard. Sticking out of the stone was a large sword. On the stone were these words: Whoever can pull the sword from this stone is the true king of Britain.

All the knights tried to remove the sword. But not one of them could even move it. Finally, the archbishop invited all the knights in the land to a jousting tournament. Each knight would have a chance to pull the sword from the stone.

A proud knight named Sir Kay traveled to the tournament with his younger brother, Arthur, and their father, Sir Hector. Just before the event began, Sir Kay realized he had forgotten his sword. He ordered Arthur to go back to their inn to get it. But when Arthur got there, the doors were locked and no one answered. Everyone was at the tournament.

While he was thinking about what to do, Arthur spotted the large sword sticking out of the stone in the churchyard. Arthur grabbed the handle and gave it a sharp tug. The sword slid from the stone smoothly and silently.

Arthur quickly rode back to the tournament and handed the sword to Sir Kay. Sir Kay recognized the weapon and quickly hid it under his cloak.

9. You can tell that the archbishop planned the tournament in order to
   Ⓐ find the strongest knight in the land.
   Ⓑ find the new king of Britain.
   Ⓒ entertain the people of Britain.
   Ⓓ show off the skills of each knight.

10. Details in the legend suggest that Merlin
    Ⓐ did not trust the archbishop.
    Ⓑ had lied about the baby's life being in danger.
    Ⓒ wanted to be the future king.
    Ⓓ had used his powers to set the stone in the churchyard.

11. What can you conclude about Sir Kay?
    Ⓐ He was treated badly by his brother.
    Ⓑ He had forgotten his sword at the inn on purpose.
    Ⓒ He would claim that he had pulled the sword from the stone.
    Ⓓ He would win the jousting tournament.

12. You can tell that Arthur
    Ⓐ wanted to enter the tournament, too.
    Ⓑ knew that Sir Hector wasn't his father.
    Ⓒ was actually King Uther's son.
    Ⓓ would also become a knight one day.

TEST TIPS	• A test question about drawing conclusions and making inferences asks you to figure out something that is not stated in a passage. • A test question about drawing conclusions and making inferences often contains the words *you can tell*, *determine*, or *conclude*.

Read this business letter. Then answer questions about the letter. Choose the best answer for Numbers 13 and 14.

1776 Conservation Way
Anytown, WI 50000
January 1, 2010

Ms. Lotta Waste, President
Pretty U Cosmetics
One Landfill Place
Big City, IL 60000

Dear Ms. Waste:

 I am writing to express my concerns about how much packaging you use for your products. Most of this wrapping ends up being thrown away. Don't you realize that too much trash is a big problem in our country? An average American family throws away more than one ton of trash a year. About 80 percent of it is dumped into landfills. Often, the buried trash does not break down quickly. Plastics can stay buried in the land for hundreds of years.

 Please start to use less packaging for your products. Use materials that can be recycled. Try to encourage your customers to find ways to use the packaging again.

 I hope you will listen to my suggestions. Together, we can help save the earth.

Sincerely,
Rhea Cycle

13. You can tell that the writer of the letter
Ⓐ works at a landfill.
Ⓑ does not wear cosmetics.
Ⓒ is concerned about the environment.
Ⓓ wonders why trash is such a big problem.

14. There is enough information in the letter to show that
Ⓐ plastic breaks down more slowly than other materials.
Ⓑ the writer's suggestions will be ignored.
Ⓒ burning trash is better than dumping it.
Ⓓ buried trash never breaks down.

Read this science article about asteroids. Then answer questions about the article. Choose the best answer for Numbers 15 and 16.

You probably know a lot about the planets that orbit the sun. But how much do you know about the other things that are zooming around our solar system?

Asteroids, for example, are huge chunks of rock. They can measure from 3,000 feet to 600 miles across. Comets are huge bodies of ice that range in size from 3,000 feet to 60 miles across. Their tails are made of gas and dust that can stretch millions of miles. Meteoroids are pieces of rock, metal, or ice. Most meteoroids have broken off from comets or asteroids. They can be as small as a grain of sand or as large as a house.

asteroid

What if an asteroid or a comet several miles large struck Earth? The explosion would have the power of many atomic bombs. Such an event may have been the reason that the dinosaurs disappeared. It wouldn't matter if the object landed in the ocean. The explosion would cause so much dust that there'd be no sunlight for months. Tidal waves would destroy coastal cities.

Several movies have been made about a huge asteroid or comet speeding toward Earth. Experts try to find a way to avoid the impact. One plan involves destroying the object with a bomb. In real life, blowing apart an asteroid or a comet too close to Earth would not save the planet. The blown-up bits of rock and ice would still cause damage.

The details in these disaster films are not really accurate. The threat of Earth's being battered from above, however, is real. Concerned scientists are always on the lookout for any real comet or asteroid that could strike Earth.

15. From this article, you can tell that
   Ⓐ asteroids and comets are always hitting Earth.
   Ⓑ an asteroid or a comet could one day hit Earth.
   Ⓒ blowing up asteroids and comets is a good solution.
   Ⓓ comets that land in the ocean are not dangerous.

16. You can conclude that meteoroids
   Ⓐ can be easily destroyed by scientists.
   Ⓑ are always visible to the human eye.
   Ⓒ are less dangerous than asteroids.
   Ⓓ have long tails like comets.

DISTINGUISHING BETWEEN FACT AND OPINION

PART ONE: Think About the Strategy

What Is a Fact?

Have you ever told someone your age or how many people are in your family? If so, you were telling facts. A fact is something that can be proved. If you say, "I have two brothers and one sister," you are telling a fact. It can be proved.

1 Write one fact about yourself.

_____

What Is an Opinion?

Have you ever told someone how you feel about something? If so, you were telling an opinion. An opinion is what you think or believe. An opinion cannot be proved. If you say, "I make the best chocolate chip cookies," you are expressing an opinion. Everyone might not agree with you.

2 Write one opinion about yourself.

_____

3 Write how your fact is different from your opinion.

_____

_____

_____

Work with a Partner

- Take turns telling a fact about something, such as sports or famous landmarks.
- Then tell an opinion about the same thing.

- Distinguish between fact and opinion (**GPI.R.1**)
- Evaluate content by identifying statements of fact and opinion (**GPI.R.3**)
- Explain the difference between fact and fiction (**GPI.R.2**)
- Judge accuracy of content to gather facts (**GPI.R.3**)

How Do You Find Facts and Opinions?

Some reading passages have details that are facts. Some passages have details that are opinions. Many passages contain both facts and opinions. You can tell the difference between a fact and an opinion by asking yourself one question: "Does this detail tell about something that can be proved?" If your answer is "yes," then the detail is a fact. If your answer is "no," then the detail is an opinion.

Read this passage about a pet snake. See if you can tell the facts from the opinions.

> Snakes are creepy. But not to my sister. She has a pet snake. She takes it out of its cage and holds it. It curls around her neck and her arm. It's horrible to watch!

1. Let's think about which details in the passage are facts and which details are opinions.

2. Look at the chart below.

    Read each detail.

    If the detail an be proved, place a check mark next to "Fact."

    If the detail cannot be proved, place a check mark next to "Opinion."

Detail	Fact or Opinion		
Snakes are creepy.	Yes, it can be proved.	☐	Fact
	No, it cannot be proved.	✓	Opinion
She has a pet snake.	Yes, it can be proved.	✓	Fact
	No, it cannot be proved.	☐	Opinion
She takes it out of its cage and holds it.	Yes, it can be proved.	☐	Fact
	No, it cannot be proved.	☐	Opinion
It curls around her neck and her arm.	Yes, it can be proved.	☐	Fact
	No, it cannot be proved.	☐	Opinion
It's horrible to watch!	Yes, it can be proved.	☐	Fact
	No, it cannot be proved.	☐	Opinion

| **WHAT TO KNOW** | If a statement can be proved, it is a **fact**. If a statement tells what someone thinks or feels about something, it is an **opinion**. Facts can be proved. Opinions cannot. When you figure out if a statement is a fact or an opinion, you are **distinguishing between fact and opinion**. |

- Facts are statements that can be checked or proved.

- Opinions are statements that cannot be proved.
  They tell what someone thinks or feels.

- Opinions often contain clue words, such as *think, feel, believe,* and *seem.* Other common clue words are *always, never, all, none, most, least, greatest, best,* and *worst.*

Read this paragraph about a popular snack. As you read, look for statements that can be proved. Also look for statements that tell what someone thinks or feels.

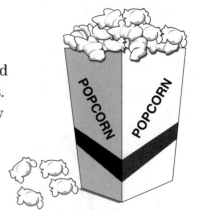

Popcorn is the best snack to eat at fairs, movies, and ball games. I believe that popcorn is the most healthful treat. Popcorn is actually good for you, if you leave out the butter and salt. People have been popping popcorn for thousands of years. The native people in what is now Mexico were the first to grow popcorn plants. The popcorn kernels were too hard to eat. One native tossed a handful of the hard kernels into a fire. Pop! America's most tasty treat was born.

The statements that can be proved are:

Popcorn is actually good for you, if you leave out the butter and salt.

People have been popping popcorn for thousands of years.

The native people in what is now Mexico were the first to grow popcorn plants.

The popcorn kernels were too hard to eat.

One native tossed a handful of the hard kernels into a fire.

The statements that tell what someone thinks or feels are:

Popcorn is the best snack to eat at fairs, movies, and ball games.

I believe that popcorn is the most healthful treat.

America's most tasty treat was born.

Read this website page designed for daring travelers. As you read, ask yourself, "Which statements can be proved? Which statements cannot be proved?" Then answer the questions.

Polar Travel

Tired of visiting the same old places? Need some excitement in your life? Ready to show just how tough you are? If you've answered yes to any of these questions, then we have an adventure for you. Come join Polar Travel on a flight to the North Pole. We think the North Pole is the "coolest" place on the planet!

Our pilots are the greatest in the world, and the planes we fly are the safest. It will take us ten days to reach the Pole, with stops along the way. As we cross the High Arctic, we may spot a few polar bears and people. As we get closer to the Pole, though, we'll see only miles and miles of snow and ice. (It's so cold at the North Pole that the ocean surrounding it is frozen most of the year.) This white desert is the most beautiful spot on Earth.

Our next flight to the North Pole leaves in early April. By then, it's no longer dark all the time. Also, the ice has not yet begun to thaw and crack. Our planes have special landing gear, but we don't want our icy runway to open up.

So, pack your bags and get ready to go. Make sure you pack lots of warm clothes. Nothing is as brutal as the weather in the North Pole.

1. Which statement is a *fact*?
   - Ⓐ We think the North Pole is the "coolest" place on the planet!
   - Ⓑ It's so cold at the North Pole that the ocean surrounding it is frozen most of the year.
   - Ⓒ This white desert is the most beautiful spot on Earth.
   - Ⓓ Nothing is as brutal as the weather in the North Pole.

2. Which clue word in the ad signals an *opinion* about the skills of Polar Travel pilots?
   - Ⓐ think
   - Ⓑ believe
   - Ⓒ greatest
   - Ⓓ most

Work with a Partner

- Talk about your answers to the questions.
- Tell why you chose your answers.
- Then talk about what you have learned so far about distinguishing between fact and opinion.

REVIEW

Facts can be proved. Opinions cannot be proved.

- To find out if a statement is a fact, ask yourself, "Can this statement be proved?"

- To find out if a statement is an opinion, ask yourself, "Does this statement tell what someone thinks or feels?"

- Look for clue words that signal an opinion, such as *think, feel, believe, seem, always, never, all, none, most, least, greatest, best,* and *worst.*

Read this article about a terrible event in history. As you read, think about which statements are facts and which are opinions. Then answer the questions.

During the Middle Ages, the people in Europe forgot what their ancestors had learned about staying healthy. No one worried about having fresh water. No one cared about getting rid of waste from the streets. No one took baths anymore. With these unclean conditions, diseases spread quickly. When a disease broke out, it often killed thousands of people. The worst of these epidemics was known as the Black Death. It first hit Europe in 1348.

Rats first carried the disease that caused the Black Death. Most of these pests had come to Europe on ships. Everyone lived in constant fear that death could strike them down at any time. In just 3 years, 25 million people died. In 25 years, the Black Death killed between one third and one half of Europe's entire population. Europeans have never known a sadder time in their history.

3. Which of these statements about the Middle Ages can be proved?

Ⓐ No one cared about getting rid of waste from the streets.

Ⓑ No one took baths anymore.

Ⓒ When a disease broke out, it often killed thousands of people.

Ⓓ Everyone lived in constant fear that death could strike them down at any time.

4. Which of these statements tells what someone thinks or feels?

Ⓐ The Black Death first hit Europe in 1348.

Ⓑ Rats first carried the disease that caused the Black Death.

Ⓒ In just 3 years, 25 million people died.

Ⓓ Europeans have never known a sadder time in their history.

Distinguishing Between Fact and Opinion

Which Answer Is Correct and Why?

**Look at the answer choices for each question.
Read why each answer choice is correct or not correct.**

3. **Which of these statements about the Middle Ages can be proved?**

   Ⓐ **No one cared about getting rid of waste from the streets.**

   This answer is not correct because it cannot be proved that no one cared about getting rid of waste. Most likely, some people did care.

   Ⓑ **No one took baths anymore.**

   This answer is not correct because it cannot be proved that no one took baths. People must have washed up every now and then; some more often than others.

   ● **When a disease broke out, it often killed thousands of people.**

   This answer is correct because you can prove this statement is true. You can find facts about what happened when diseases broke out during the Middle Ages in a book, in an encyclopedia, or on the Internet.

   Ⓓ **Everyone lived in constant fear that death could strike them down at any time.**

   This answer is not correct because, although some people may have lived in constant fear of dying, it's doubtful that everyone was afraid all of the time.

4. **Which of these statements tells what someone thinks or feels?**

   Ⓐ **The Black Death first hit Europe in 1348.**

   This answer is not correct because this statement is a fact that can be proved. You can find facts about the Black Death in a book, in an encyclopedia, or on the Internet.

   Ⓑ **Rats first carried the disease that caused the Black Death.**

   This answer is not correct because this statement is a fact that can be proved. You can find facts about the Black Death in a book, in an encyclopedia, or on the Internet.

   Ⓒ **In just 3 years, 25 million people died.**

   This answer is not correct because this statement is a fact that can be proved. You can find facts about the Black Death in a book, in an encyclopedia, or on the Internet.

   ● **Europeans have never known a sadder time in their history.**

   This answer is correct because it states what the writer believes to be the saddest time in European history. It cannot be proved. The clue word *never* signals that this statement is an opinion, not a fact.

MORE TO KNOW

- Facts can be observed, checked, or tested.
  You can prove that a fact is correct or true.

- Opinions express someone's thoughts, feelings, or beliefs.
  An opinion can be about an event, an idea, a person, or a thing.
  Even though people might agree or disagree with an opinion,
  it still cannot be proved.

Read this report about Jim Thorpe. Then answer the questions.

Jim Thorpe was born in Oklahoma on May 28, 1888. He lived with his family on an Indian reservation. Jim's Native-American name was Wa-Tho-Hack. This means "bright path." Jim's parents chose this name just for their son. They believed he had a promising future.

Jim always liked to play sports. He ran in races and played football and baseball. Jim was an excellent athlete. He showed great talent in every sport he played. I think Jim was the most amazing athlete. He was so good at so many sports. Jim didn't really think about his future until he was in college. That's when he decided to play sports for a living. He went on to win gold medals in the 1912 Olympics in Sweden. Sweden's king called Jim "the greatest athlete in the world." Jim had finally found his bright path. He became one of the best athletes ever.

5. Which of these is a *fact* from the report?
   Ⓐ Jim ran in races and played football and baseball.
   Ⓑ Jim was an excellent athlete.
   Ⓒ Jim became one of the best athletes ever.
   Ⓓ I think Jim was the most amazing athlete.

6. Which of these cannot be proved?
   Ⓐ He was so good at so many sports.
   Ⓑ Jim Thorpe was born in Oklahoma.
   Ⓒ Jim's Native-American name was Wa-Tho-Hack.
   Ⓓ He went on to win gold medals in the 1912 Olympics in Sweden.

7. Which of these clue words in the report signals an *opinion* of Sweden's king?
   Ⓐ most
   Ⓑ best
   Ⓒ greatest
   Ⓓ believed

8. A *fact* about Jim Thorpe that can be proved is
   Ⓐ he lived with his family on an Indian reservation.
   Ⓑ he was the greatest athlete in the world.
   Ⓒ he was so good at so many sports.
   Ⓓ he became one of the best athletes ever.

Read this movie review written by a student for her weekly school newspaper. Then answer the questions.

This Week's Video Pick

Star Wars is the best movie ever made. There's something to please everyone in this science-fiction flick. George Lucas is the creator of *Star Wars*. I think that George Lucas is a genius. He has the greatest imagination. He has invented the most amazing characters, robots, spaceships, and special effects.

Millions of people have seen *Star Wars*. *Star Wars* is one of the top five movies in ticket and rental sales. On the day the film was released in May 1977, people lined up for hours at theaters to see it. When the movie ended, some people got right back in line.

The movie's plot is about the fight between the Rebel Alliance and the evil Empire. The Rebel princess holds stolen plans for the Death Star. The Death Star is the battle station that Darth Vader wants to build. Darth Vader is the leader of the Empire, and he wants the stolen plans back.

When the princess's ship is attacked, she hides the plans in a robot called R2-D2. Princess Leia is captured, but R2-D2 escapes with C-3PO, a fellow droid, to the planet Tatooine. There they meet Luke Skywalker. R2-D2 leads the young man to an old man named Obi-Wan Kenobi. Obi-Wan is a former Jedi knight. He is also the wisest of men. He tells Luke about Darth Vader, the most dreaded member of the Empire, and teaches Luke the ways of the Force. Next, Luke and Obi-Wan hire a big furry beast named Chewbacca and a bold pilot named Han Solo to help them. They need to deliver the Death Star plans to the Rebel Alliance before Darth Vader can get the plans back.

I won't reveal the rest of the story, just in case you are one of the few people who haven't seen it. If you haven't seen *Star Wars*, rent it today. Seeing the film is an experience you won't forget. May the Force be with you!

9. Which of these statements about George Lucas can be proved?

Ⓐ I think that George Lucas is a genius.

Ⓑ He has invented the most amazing characters, robots, spaceships, and special effects.

Ⓒ George Lucas is the creator of *Star Wars*.

Ⓓ He has the greatest imagination.

10. Which of these is a *fact* from the movie review?

Ⓐ *Star Wars* is one of the top five movies in ticket and rental sales.

Ⓑ There's something to please everyone in this science-fiction flick.

Ⓒ *Star Wars* is the best movie ever made.

Ⓓ Seeing the film is an experience you won't forget.

11. Which of these statements is an *opinion* about Obi-Wan Kenobi?

Ⓐ Obi-wan is a former Jedi knight.

Ⓑ He teaches Luke Skywalker the ways of the Force.

Ⓒ He is also the wisest of men.

Ⓓ He tells Luke Skywalker about Darth Vader.

12. Which of these is an *opinion* about Darth Vader?

Ⓐ He is the leader of the Empire.

Ⓑ He is the most dreaded member of the Empire.

Ⓒ He wants to build the Death Star.

Ⓓ He wants the stolen plans back.

**TEST
TIPS**

- A test question about fact and opinion may ask you to identify which of four statements is a fact or an opinion.

- To recognize a *fact*, read each answer choice and ask yourself, "Can this statement be proved?" If it can, then it is a fact.

- To recognize an *opinion*, read each answer choice and ask yourself, "Does this statement tell what someone thinks or feels?" If it does, then it is an opinion. Look in the answer choices for clue words that signal an opinion.

**Read this report on penguins. Then answer questions about the report.
Choose the best answer for Numbers 13 and 14.**

The penguin is the most unusual bird. It walks upright and cannot fly. I think the penguin is the funniest-looking bird in the world. With its black back and white belly, it looks like a small, round waiter wearing a tuxedo. The penguin must be the clumsiest animal on land. It waddles around on two short legs and webbed feet.

Although penguins walk funny and can't fly, they are excellent swimmers. Penguins are more graceful in the water than any other sea animal. Instead of wings, penguins have powerful flippers. They help penguins swim underwater at fast speeds.

Penguins live in cold waters in the Southern Hemisphere. Several kinds live in Antarctica, the coldest place on Earth. A penguin's body has many layers to protect it from freezing temperatures. Thick layers of fat under thick skin help keep in heat. A thick coat of short, oily feathers keeps its skin dry. Beneath this waterproof coat are downy feathers. They trap warm air around the body.

There are 18 kinds of penguins. The largest is the emperor penguin. It stands about four feet high and weighs about 100 pounds. It has a collar of bright orange and yellow feathers around its neck. In 1997, scientists in Antarctica discovered an all-white emperor penguin. So far, this rare penguin is the only one ever seen.

13. Which of these is an *opinion*?
- Ⓐ Penguins live in cold waters in the Southern Hemisphere.
- Ⓑ The largest penguin is the emperor penguin.
- Ⓒ The penguin waddles around on two short legs and webbed feet.
- Ⓓ I think the penguin is the funniest-looking bird in the world.

14. Which of these is a *fact*?
- Ⓐ The penguin must be the clumsiest animal on land.
- Ⓑ A penguin's body has many layers to protect it from freezing temperatures.
- Ⓒ Penguins are more graceful in the water than any other sea animal.
- Ⓓ The penguin is the most unusual-looking bird.

Distinguishing Between Fact and Opinion

Read this newspaper article about a historic event. Then answer questions about the article. Choose the best answer for Numbers 15 and 16.

World News   July 21, 1969

Men Land on Moon!

Last night at 10:56 Eastern Daylight Time, astronaut Neil Armstrong became the first person to set foot on the moon. About 600 million TV viewers saw the moon landing. It was the proudest moment in United States history. As Armstrong placed his left foot onto the moon's surface, he told the world, "That's one small step for man, one giant leap for mankind." His words will always be remembered.

Minutes later, Edwin "Buzz" Aldrin, Jr., joined Armstrong on the moon's surface. The third crew member, Michael Collins, remained in orbit aboard the command ship, *Columbia.*

Armstrong and Aldrin are the bravest people alive. They explored the moon for more than two hours. They planted an American flag on the moon's surface. They took pictures. They collected soil and rock samples. They also ran experiments.

Armstrong, Aldrin, and Collins blasted off from Cape Kennedy in *Apollo 11* on July 16. The spacecraft traveled at the speed of 35,533 feet per second. Altogether, it took 103 hours and 30 minutes to travel from Earth to the moon.

On July 20, Armstrong and Aldrin stepped on board their lunar module, the *Eagle.* Soon they were headed to the moon's surface. They landed on the Sea of Tranquility. This sea has no water. It is named for one of the flat, dark areas on the moon.

The *Apollo 11* astronauts plan to return to Earth on July 24. They'll probably receive the best homecoming anyone has ever had. It is believed that these three men will become heroes to every child in the nation.

15. Which statement is a *fact?*
   Ⓐ Armstrong, Aldrin, and Collins blasted off from Cape Kennedy in *Apollo 11* on July 16.
   Ⓑ Armstrong's words will always be remembered.
   Ⓒ Armstrong and Aldrin are the bravest people alive.
   Ⓓ It is believed that these three men will become heroes to every child in the nation.

16. Which of these expresses an *opinion?*
   Ⓐ Armstrong became the first person to set foot on the moon.
   Ⓑ Armstrong and Aldrin explored the moon for more than two hours.
   Ⓒ About 600 million TV viewers saw the moon landing.
   Ⓓ It was the proudest moment in United States history.

Read this journal entry. Then answer questions about the journal entry. Choose the best answer for Numbers 1 through 6.

Monday, October 13

Today was the best day! A new boy joined our class. His name is Paul, and I've never met a nicer kid. Our teacher had told us last week that Paul was coming from a place very far away. I thought he would probably have very different customs. When Paul walked into our classroom, though, he looked just like any other boy in the class. He wore a T-shirt and jeans. His sneakers were just like the ones I was wearing.

Then Paul spoke. Although he used English, I had trouble understanding him. Paul has the most unusual accent, and he uses expressions that I've never heard before.

When Paul introduced himself to the class, he said, "G'day" for "Good day." Paul told us that he liked many of the same sports as American boys and girls, or as Paul says, "blokes" and "sheilahs." He has a younger brother in the first grade, and Paul told us that the little "nipper" is the biggest pest. Paul also explained that his family's flight to the States was the bumpiest plane ride ever. He felt "crook" during the entire flight.

Finally, I asked Paul the question everyone wanted answered. "Where are you from?"

"I'm from Oz," answered Paul.

"Hey," someone called out, "that's not a real place."

Everyone laughed, including Paul. "I must have kangaroos in my top paddock!" he exclaimed. "What I meant to say is that I'm from Australia."

Finding Word Meaning
in Context

Drawing Conclusions
and Making Inferences

Distinguishing Between
Fact and Opinion

Finding Word Meaning in Context

1. The word *sheilahs* in paragraph 3 means
   - Ⓐ "brothers."
   - Ⓑ "girls."
   - Ⓒ "kangaroos."
   - Ⓓ "very young children."

Finding Word Meaning in Context

2. You can tell that the word *crook* means
   - Ⓐ "bent."
   - Ⓑ "delighted."
   - Ⓒ "ill."
   - Ⓓ "like a thief."

Drawing Conclusions and Making Inferences

3. From the journal entry, you can tell that
   - Ⓐ Paul has a sense of humor.
   - Ⓑ Paul doesn't like to be teased.
   - Ⓒ Paul hates to fly in airplanes.
   - Ⓓ Paul's favorite sport is soccer.

Drawing Conclusions and Making Inferences

4. Which detail helped you answer question 3?
   - Ⓐ Paul told us that the little "nipper" is the biggest pest.
   - Ⓑ Paul told us that he liked many of the same sports as American boys and girls.
   - Ⓒ I asked Paul the question everyone wanted answered.
   - Ⓓ Everyone laughed, including Paul.

Distinguishing Between Fact and Opinion

5. Which clue word in the journal entry signals an *opinion* about Paul's accent?
   - Ⓐ think
   - Ⓑ best
   - Ⓒ never
   - Ⓓ most

Distinguishing Between Fact and Opinion

6. Which of these is a *fact*?
   - Ⓐ Paul's younger brother is the biggest pest.
   - Ⓑ Paul's flight to the States was the bumpiest plane ride ever.
   - Ⓒ Paul dresses like the other boys in his class.
   - Ⓓ Paul is the nicest kid.

Read this short biography of a famous president. Then answer questions about the biography. Choose the best answer for Numbers 7 through 12.

You know that George Washington was the first president of the United States. He was in office from 1789 to 1797. You probably also know that he was a general in the American Revolution. Here are some facts, though, that you may not know.

Washington was a wise man. Yet, he never went to college. Washington went to school near the Virginia farms where he grew up. He took his first job at age 17.

In his early twenties, Washington fought to protect the frontier against the French and the Indians. Washington was a reckless soldier. During one battle, he was particularly careless. Two horses were shot from under him, and four bullets pierced his coat. But he rode on unharmed. Later, Washington became our nation's bravest general.

Washington was a very tall man for his time. Some people thought he appeared stiff and unfeeling. In truth, Washington always treated others with warmth and kindness.

Washington liked things to be just so. Mount Vernon, his plantation where he often experimented with new crops, always looked beautiful. Washington rode in the fanciest carriages pulled by the finest horses. He also dressed in elegant clothes. Even his false teeth were the best he could get. They were made from the tusk of a hippopotamus.

Washington chose the site for the capital later named in his honor. But he never worked there. He led the country from New York City during his first term. He led from Philadelphia during his second term.

Washington always did his best, but he was never hungry for power. In 1782, it was suggested that General Washington become king. He said no immediately. He also later refused a third term as president.

In 1799, Washington died suddenly. He was 67 years old. After his death, a friend delivered a speech to Congress. It summed up the great leader's contributions to the new nation: "Washington was first in war, first in peace, and first in the hearts of his countrymen."

Finding Word Meaning in Context

7. In paragraph 3, which words give a clue to the meaning of the word *reckless*?

    Ⓐ our nation's bravest general

    Ⓑ fought to protect the frontier

    Ⓒ was particularly careless

    Ⓓ rode on unharmed

Drawing Conclusions and Making Inferences

10. From the biography, you can tell that

    Ⓐ Washington was easily embarrassed.

    Ⓑ Washington's teeth caused him a lot of pain.

    Ⓒ Washington didn't like living in New York City.

    Ⓓ Washington never lived in the White House.

Finding Word Meaning in Context

8. You can tell that a plantation is

    Ⓐ a farm.

    Ⓑ a mountain home.

    Ⓒ a beautiful garden.

    Ⓓ the capital of Virginia.

Distinguishing Between Fact and Opinion

11. Which of these statements is an *opinion*?

    Ⓐ Mount Vernon was the name of Washington's plantation.

    Ⓑ Washington became our nation's bravest general.

    Ⓒ Washington had false teeth made from the tusk of a hippopotamus.

    Ⓓ Washington chose the site of our nation's present capital.

Drawing Conclusions and Making Inferences

9. There is enough information in the biography to show that Washington

    Ⓐ was a respected man.

    Ⓑ was stern with his soldiers.

    Ⓒ was a foolish man.

    Ⓓ regretted that he didn't go to college.

Distinguishing Between Fact and Opinion

12. Which of these is a *fact*?

    Ⓐ Washington should not have been so careless.

    Ⓑ Washington always did his best.

    Ⓒ Washington did not want to be king.

    Ⓓ Washington was the best American president.

What Is Author's Purpose?

Authors always write for a reason. Everything you read has a purpose.
An author's purpose is either to describe, to entertain, to explain, or to persuade.

Write what you think the author's purpose is for writing each of the following.
Tell if the author's purpose is to describe, to entertain, to explain, or to persuade.

1 A newspaper article

The author's purpose is to _____.

2 A book about a funny adventure

The author's purpose is to _____.

3 An advertisement

The author's purpose is to _____.

4 A paragraph about what Jupiter looks like

The author's purpose is to _____.

Work with a Partner

- Take turns talking about some of the different things you have read.
  Think about things such as books, newspaper ads, movie reviews, and poems.
- Together, see if you can identify the author's purpose for what you read.

- Evaluate content by identifying the author's purpose (**GPI.R.3**)
- Use graphic organizers to record significant details from informational texts (**GPI.R.2**)

How Do You Find Author's Purpose?

Every reading passage is written for a reason. When you read, ask yourself, "What does the author want me to know?" Your answer will help you figure out the author's purpose.

Read this passage about ice-skating. See if you can figure out the author's purpose for writing it.

> Ice-skating was once a way for people who lived in cold places to get from place to place easier. The first ice skaters lived in Norway and Sweden. These two countries have a lot of ice in the winter. People in these countries used the bones of cows' ribs to make their ice skates.

1. Think about what the author wants you to know.

   Let's narrow down the choices by using the chart below.

2. Check "yes" or "no" for each choice. You can check "yes" only once in this chart.

	Yes	No	
Does the passage mostly give details about a particular person, place, or thing?			Describe
Does the passage tell a humorous story or teach a lesson?			Entertain
Does the passage give facts about something or tell how to do something?			Explain
Does the passage try to get you to do or buy something?			Persuade

3. Write the choice that has a check mark for "yes."

_____

WHAT TO KNOW

All authors write for a reason. The reason an author writes something is called the author's purpose. When you figure out why a reading passage was written, you are **identifying the author's purpose**. Authors write for one of four reasons—to describe, to entertain, to explain, or to persuade.

- Some reading passages mainly describe something, such as a person, place, or thing. The author's purpose is to **describe**.

- Some reading passages mainly tell a personal story, tell something funny, or use a story to teach a lesson. The author's purpose is to **entertain**.

- Some reading passages mainly tell how to do something or contain lots of information about a person, place, or thing. The author's purpose is to **explain**.

- Some reading passages are mainly written to try to get readers to do something, buy something, or believe something. The author's purpose is to **persuade**.

Read this nonsense poem about things that don't really happen. As you read, think about why the author probably wrote the poem.

'Tis Midnight

'Tis midnight and the setting sun
   Is slowly rising in the west.
The rapid rivers slowly run,
   The frog is on his downy nest.
The pensive goat and sportive cow,
   Hilarious, leap from bough to bough.

Author Unknown

The author probably wrote this poem to make you smile or think it was funny. The author's purpose is to entertain readers with a silly poem.

Read this article about newspapers. As you read, try to figure out the author's purpose for writing the article. Then answer the questions.

All About the News

Many people start their day by reading the newspaper. The newspaper is filled with ads, comics, and articles. Some articles are written to tell readers news about important events. The events may take place in their community. Other articles explain what is happening across the nation or around the world.

Another purpose of newspapers is to describe things. Articles often give a lot of details about events, people, and places.

Newspapers also try to persuade readers. The editorial pages are filled with writers' opinions. Writers try to convince people to think or feel a certain way. Ads are found throughout the newspaper. Ads try to get people to buy goods.

Newspapers also have fun things to entertain readers. For some readers, the comic strips and word puzzles are their favorite parts.

1. The author wrote the article mainly to
   Ⓐ explain what is found in a newspaper.
   Ⓑ describe what it is like to work for a newspaper company.
   Ⓒ try to get readers to buy newspapers.
   Ⓓ entertain readers with an enjoyable story about newspapers.

2. You know your answer to question 1 is correct because the article mainly
   Ⓐ describes in detail a person, place, or thing.
   Ⓑ contains lots of facts and information about something.
   Ⓒ tries to convince readers of something.
   Ⓓ tells a story that most readers would enjoy.

Work with a Partner

- Talk about your answers to the questions.
- Tell why you chose your answers.
- Then talk about what you have learned so far about identifying author's purpose.

REVIEW

Authors write to describe, to entertain, to explain, or to persuade.

- To figure out if the author's purpose is to describe, ask yourself, "Does the author provide lots of details about a particular person, place, or thing?"

- To figure out if the author's purpose is to entertain, ask yourself, "Does the author tell a personal story or try to make me laugh? Does the author use a story to teach a lesson?"

- To figure out if the author's purpose is to explain, ask yourself, "Does the author tell me facts about a person, place, or thing? Does the author tell me how to do or make something?"

- To figure out if the author's purpose is to persuade, ask yourself, "Does the author try to get me to do something, buy something, or believe something?"

Read this ad from a travel brochure. As you read, ask yourself, "Why did the author probably write this ad?" Then answer the questions.

Come to Jamaica!

Come visit the beautiful island of Jamaica. Nowhere else will you find so many natural wonders. Jamaica has miles and miles of soft, sandy beaches. There are also forests, mountains, and rivers. And don't forget the spectacular waterfalls! It's no surprise that the island's name means "land of wood and water."

While you're here, you'll enjoy day after day of warm weather. Jamaica has a tropical climate. This means there are no cold seasons. You also don't want to miss the chance to go shopping. The outdoor marketplaces are exciting! Or just listen to the rhythm of Jamaican "talk." Whatever you decide to do, Jamaica is the place for you.

3. The author wrote the ad mainly to
   - Ⓐ persuade readers to go to Jamaica.
   - Ⓑ explain the history of Jamaica.
   - Ⓒ describe Jamaica's waterfalls.
   - Ⓓ entertain readers with tales about Jamaica.

4. You know your answer to question 3 is correct because the ad mainly
   - Ⓐ contains many details that describe something.
   - Ⓑ provides facts or tells readers how to do something.
   - Ⓒ tries to convince readers of something.
   - Ⓓ tells an enjoyable story.

Which Answer Is Correct and Why?

Look at the answer choices for each question.
Read why each answer choice is correct or not correct.

3. The author wrote the ad mainly to

● **persuade readers to go to Jamaica.**
This answer is correct because the ad contains a lot of reasons that try to convince people to visit the island.

Ⓑ **explain the history of Jamaica.**
This answer is not correct because the ad does not contain facts or other information to explain the history of Jamaica.

Ⓒ **describe Jamaica's waterfalls.**
This answer is not correct because, while the ad does describe waterfalls as spectacular, this is not the main purpose for why the author wrote the ad.

Ⓓ **entertain readers with tales about Jamaica.**
This answer is not correct because the ad does not tell an interesting story or try to make readers laugh, nor does the author use a story to teach a lesson.

4. You know your answer to question 3 is correct because the ad mainly

Ⓐ **contains many details that describe something.**
This answer is not correct because the ad does not mainly contain many details that describe a particular person, place, or thing.

Ⓑ **provides facts or tells readers how to do something.**
This answer is not correct because the ad does not mainly contain facts or information that teaches or explains how to do something.

● **tries to convince readers of something.**
This answer is correct because the ad contains mainly opinions about Jamaica's beauty. These details are provided to convince people that Jamaica is the place to go for a beautiful and warm vacation spot.

Ⓓ **tells an enjoyable story.**
This answer is not correct because the ad does not tell an interesting story or try to make readers laugh, nor does the author use a story to teach a lesson.

| MORE TO KNOW | Different reading passages are written for different purposes. Knowing the kind of passage you are reading often helps you identify the author's purpose. |

- Articles are usually written to describe or explain people, places, or things.
- Directions are written to explain how to do or make something.
- Personal stories, riddles, and poetry are written to entertain.
- Ads and articles in which an opinion is stated are written to persuade.

Read each passage. Then answer the questions.

Come One, Come All

Who: Anyone who is a kid at heart
What: Sand Castle Contest
Where: Sunset Beach
When: August 8
Why: To win a trip to Hawaii!
How: Bring pails and shovels, and let your imagination go!

Just for Laughs

What do you call a grouchy person at the beach?
A sand crab.

What did the ocean say to the sand?
Nothing; it just waved.

Sand Art

Gather spoons, a paintbrush, a glass jar, and bags of colored sand. Then spoon thin layers of sand into the jar. Spread each sand layer evenly with the paintbrush. Work carefully to avoid mixing colors. To vary the design, press the wooden end of the paintbrush against the jar wall and push down. The sand will move down, forming a pattern with points.

Quicksand

Quicksand is loose, wet sand. It can be found near the mouths of rivers and along beaches. Quicksand forms when water flows upward from deep in the ground. The bubbling water pushes the sand grains apart so that they flow like water. Contrary to what most people believe, quicksand does not pull things down into it. The best thing to do if caught in quicksand is to float on top of it.

5. The author's main purpose in *Come One, Come All* is to
   Ⓐ describe.　　Ⓒ entertain.
   Ⓑ explain.　　Ⓓ persuade.

6. The author's main purpose in *Sand Art* is to
   Ⓐ describe.　　Ⓒ entertain.
   Ⓑ explain.　　Ⓓ persuade.

7. The author's main purpose in *Just for Laughs* is to
   Ⓐ describe.　　Ⓒ entertain.
   Ⓑ explain.　　Ⓓ persuade.

8. The author's main purpose in *Quicksand* is to
   Ⓐ describe.　　Ⓒ entertain.
   Ⓑ explain.　　Ⓓ persuade.

Read this article that appeared in a school newspaper. Then answer the questions.

Save the Florida Manatee

The human population in Florida is growing, but the manatee population is dying out. People are taking over this sea mammal's habitat. In fact, the gentle creature has no enemies, except for people.

The manatee looks like a huge potato with flippers and a tail. Actually, this large creature is a cousin to the elephant. Manatees can reach 15 feet in length. They can weigh up to 1,600 pounds.

Manatees live in warm, shallow waters. They spend a lot of time grazing on water plants. The animals are too big to move quickly, so boats often hit them. Speeding boats kill more than 100 manatees every year. Curious people also put manatees in danger. Manatees are shy about being watched. So they'll swim out to deeper, colder waters, where it is harder for them to survive.

Many people are working hard to protect the Florida manatee. New laws have lowered the speed limits for boats in manatee habitats. No boats are allowed in at least 20 of the areas. You can help, too. Write a letter to the governor of Florida. State your interest in saving the manatee. Act now, before the manatee disappears forever.

9. The author wrote the first paragraph mainly to
   - (A) explain what is happening to manatees.
   - (B) persuade readers to stay out of Florida.
   - (C) describe how manatees behave.
   - (D) entertain readers with a myth about a manatee.

10. The author wrote paragraph 2 mainly to
   - (A) tell where manatees live.
   - (B) convince readers that manatees are related to elephants.
   - (C) describe what a manatee looks like.
   - (D) entertain readers with a funny comparison.

11. The author wrote paragraph 3 mainly to
   - (A) describe boating accidents.
   - (B) explain why manatees are in danger.
   - (C) persuade readers to help save the manatee.
   - (D) amuse readers with a tale about curious people.

12. The author wrote the last paragraph mainly to
   - (A) describe the success of boating rules in manatee habitats.
   - (B) persuade readers to protect manatees.
   - (C) amuse readers with boat-racing stories.
   - (D) explain why the manatee is disappearing.

TEST TIPS

- A test question about identifying the author's purpose may ask you why an author probably wrote a particular reading passage. This kind of question is asking about the purpose of the entire reading passage.

- A test question about identifying the author's purpose may ask you why a particular paragraph was written. This kind of question is asking about only one part of the reading passage.

Read this story about a fussy man. Then answer questions about the story. Choose the best answer for Numbers 13 and 14.

A man went into a bakery and ordered a German-chocolate cake. "I'm very particular," he told the baker. "The cake must be in the shape of the letter *B*. Can you do that for me?"

"It won't be easy," the baker answered. "I'll have to make the cake by hand, and it will take three days. But I'm sure you'll be happy with it."

Three days later, the man returned. But when he saw his cake, his face fell. "I'm sorry," he said. "It's not your fault, but I can't accept this cake. I guess I forgot to mention that it has to be in the shape of a lowercase *b*. I'll pay you anyway, but would you please try again?"

"It's your money," said the baker with a sigh. "It'll take another three days, but I want my customers to be happy."

Three days later, the customer came back. "The cake looks wonderful," he said. "It's exactly what I wanted."

"Great," replied the baker. "Let me put it in a box for you."

"That's okay" the man said. "I'm going to eat it right here."

---

13. What is the author's purpose in the first paragraph?
    (A) to describe what the man wanted
    (B) to explain why the man wanted a *B*-shaped cake
    (C) to make readers hungry for German-chocolate cake
    (D) to amuse readers with details about a man's fussy ways

14. The story was written mainly to
    (A) explain why the baker was eager to please his customer.
    (B) describe a man with a sweet tooth.
    (C) convince readers that it's not good to be too fussy.
    (D) entertain readers with a ridiculous story.

Read this imaginary interview with the scientist Marie Curie. Then answer questions about the interview. Choose the best answer for Numbers 15 and 16.

Interviewer: Dr. Curie, please tell us about your early years.

Dr. Curie: I was born in Poland in 1867. At age 15, I finished school. Girls in Poland were forbidden to go to the university. So I decided to move to a country where I was free to study.

Interviewer: Where did you go?

Dr. Curie: I went to Paris in 1891. I studied science at the Sorbonne. I worked hard and became the top student in my class.

Interviewer: What led you to the discovery that made you famous?

Dr. Curie: In 1896, Antoine-Henri Becquerel discovered that the metal uranium gave off strange and powerful rays. I decided to find out what these rays could do. I began working with a soft rock that contained uranium. I found that the rock contained another interesting material. This element gave off rays more powerful than uranium's. My husband, Pierre, and I worked together to separate this element from the rock. In 1902, we succeeded. We named the new element radium. In 1903, we were awarded the Nobel Prize in physics for our discovery. In 1911, after my husband's death, I also received the Nobel Prize in chemistry.

15. The author uses an interview format mainly to
    Ⓐ describe the events that shaped Marie Curie's life.
    Ⓑ inform readers about the power of radium.
    Ⓒ try to get people excited about studying science.
    Ⓓ entertain readers with stories about Marie Curie.

16. What is the main purpose of the last part of the interview?
    Ⓐ to convince readers that Pierre Curie also worked hard
    Ⓑ to describe for readers the events before and after the Curies' discovery
    Ⓒ to show readers that Marie Curie was proud
    Ⓓ to delight readers with a tale about a Nobel Prize winner

What Is Figurative Language?

Have you ever had something go in one ear and out the other? If so, you were not listening well. What about pulling someone's leg? If you've ever done that, you were kidding that person about something. Figurative language is the use of words in a way that is different from what the words usually mean.

1 Read this sentence.

> I tried to finish my meal, but I put too much food on my plate.

2 Now read this next sentence. It uses different words, but it has the same meaning as the first sentence.

> I tried to finish my meal, but my eyes were bigger than my stomach.

3 Write which sentence is more interesting, the first one or the second one. Tell why you chose the sentence you did.

_____

_____

_____

Work with a Partner

- Talk about some of the words you have used or heard that have a meaning different from their usual meaning. A friend might tell you that he "bent over backwards" to help someone. Your friend means that he worked very hard to help the person.

- See how many examples of figurative language you can think of.

- Use knowledge of story elements to interpret stories (**GPI.R.2**)
- Recognize how the author uses literary devices to create meaning (**GPI.R.2**)

How Do You Understand Figurative Language?

Sometimes you can use word meaning in context to help you understand figurative language. Look for clues in a reading passage to help you figure out what new meaning the words could have. Clues might be in the sentence where the words are found. They may also be in the sentence just before or just after the one in which the words are found.

Read this passage about a girl's sister named Janis. See if you can figure out what the phrase *on the wrong side of the bed* means.

> My sister Janis never wakes up for school on time. Her alarm clock rings, but she never shuts it off. My mother calls for her. Then I knock on her door. Finally, she gets up. But she always gets up on the wrong side of the bed. She's grumpy and testy. I try not to talk to her unless I have to.

1. Let's narrow down the clues to figure out what the phrase *on the wrong side of the bed* means.

   Look at the chart below. It shows three sentences:
   the one that comes before the phrase *on the wrong side of the bed*,
   the one that contains the phrase *on the wrong side of the bed*,
   and the one that comes after the phrase *on the wrong side of the bed*.

   Look carefully at the sentences that come before and after the phrase *on the wrong side of the bed*.

Finally, she gets up.	But she always gets up on the wrong side of the bed.	She's grumpy and testy.
Before		After

2. Now think about what the clues in the sentences tell you:

   It takes a long time and a lot of help before Janis finally gets up.
   When Janis does get up she is grumpy and testy.
   This means Janis is not happy when she has to get out of bed in the morning.

3. So the phrase *on the wrong side of the bed* must mean

   _____ .

WHAT TO KNOW

Similes, metaphors, and idioms are types of figurative language. Authors use figurative language to help readers create pictures in their mind. When you understand the meaning of a simile, a metaphor, or an idiom, you are **interpreting figurative language**.

- Look for things that are compared in a reading passage. Try to find examples of similes or metaphors.
- Look for phrases whose words have a meaning different from their usual meaning. Try to find examples of idioms.
- Figurative language usually brings a picture to a reader's mind. Use that picture to help you understand the meaning of the figurative language.

Read this sentence. As you read, think about the two things being compared.

> **The clouds looked like white sheep in the sky.**
> The two things being compared are clouds and sheep.
> The writer used a **simile** to help readers picture how fluffy the clouds were.
> A simile uses the word *like* or *as* to compare two different things.

Read this sentence. As you read, think about the two things being compared.

> **Falling leaves are orange clowns doing somersaults.**
> The two things being compared are falling leaves and orange clowns.
> The writer used a **metaphor** to help readers picture the sight of the leaves falling.
> A metaphor compares two different things but does not use the word *like* or *as*.
> A metaphor says that one thing *is* another thing.

Now read this sentence. As you read, think about the meaning of the underlined words.

> **Henry realized he had just <u>put his foot in his mouth</u>.**
> The underlined words mean that Henry said something he shouldn't have said.
> The underlined words are an **idiom**.
> An idiom is a phrase whose words have a meaning different from their usual meaning.

Read this selection from a poem by Lucy Larcom. As you read, ask yourself, "What pictures come to mind?" Then answer the questions.

In Time's Swing

Father Time, your footsteps go
Lightly as the falling snow.
Singing merrily, let me swing
Out of winter into spring.

Swing me out, and swing me in!
Trees are bare, but birds begin.
April chased off March today;
Now I catch a glimpse of May.

Oh, the smell of sprouting grass!
In a blur the violets pass.
Swing me low, and swing me high,
To the warm clouds of July.

Slower now, for at my side
White pond lilies open wide.
Crickets in the grass I hear;
Asters light the fading year.

Slower still! October weaves
Rainbows of the forest leaves.
Oh, 'tis snowing, swing me fast,
While December shivers past!

Frosty-bearded Father Time,
Stop your footfall on the rime!
While you swing me—gently, do!—
From the Old Year to the New.

1. In the poem, Father Time's footsteps are compared to
   - Ⓐ a swing.
   - Ⓑ winter.
   - Ⓒ birds softly chirping.
   - Ⓓ falling snow.

2. In stanza 2, the phrase *catch a glimpse* means
   - Ⓐ "chase something."
   - Ⓑ "see something briefly."
   - Ⓒ "act like a bully."
   - Ⓓ "see a dim light."

Work with a Partner

- Talk about your answers to the questions.
- Tell why you chose your answers.
- Then talk about what you have learned so far about interpreting figurative language.

REVIEW

Similes, metaphors, and idioms are types of figurative language. Authors use figurative language to help readers create pictures in their mind.

- Look for things that are compared in a reading passage.
- Look for phrases whose words have a meaning different from their usual meaning.
- Think about any pictures that come to mind as you read. Use these pictures to help you understand what is being described.

Read this fable from Aesop. As you read, look for things that are compared. Also look for words that have a meaning different from their usual meaning. Then answer the questions.

The Dog and the Wolf

A dog was lying in the sun in front of a farmyard gate. Suddenly, a wolf pounced upon the dog and was about to eat him up. The dog, though, begged for his life.

"Look at me," the dog told the wolf. "I am as thin as a rail. What a wretched meal I should make you now. In a few days, my master will be giving a feast. I'll be able to pick and choose among the table scraps. I shall get nice and fat. Then will be a better time for you to eat me."

The wolf thought this was a very good plan and went away. Sometime afterwards, he came to the farmyard again. There he found the dog lying out of reach on the roof of the barn.

"Come down and be eaten," the wolf called. "Have you forgotten our agreement?"

But the dog said coolly, "My friend, if ever you should catch me lying down by the gate again, don't wait for any feast."

Moral: *Once bitten, twice shy.*

3. In the fable, the dog's thinness is compared to
   Ⓐ table scraps.
   Ⓑ a cat.
   Ⓒ a wolf.
   Ⓓ a rail.

4. The phrase *once bitten, twice shy* means that someone who
   Ⓐ is very shy should avoid getting bitten.
   Ⓑ faced danger in the past is more careful in the future.
   Ⓒ was bitten once becomes twice as shy.
   Ⓓ bites someone else is less shy than other people.

Which Answer Is Correct and Why?

Look at the answer choices for each question.
Read why each answer choice is correct or not correct.

3. In the fable, the dog's thinness is compared to

  Ⓐ table scraps.

   This answer is not correct because there is no comparison between the dog and table scraps. Table scraps are what the dog says he will eat.

  Ⓑ a cat.

   This answer is not correct because the paragraph doesn't mention a cat, nor does it suggest that the dog's thinness is like a cat's.

  Ⓒ a wolf.

   This answer is not correct because the dog's thinness is not compared to the wolf. The dog only describes his thinness to the wolf.

  ● a rail.

   This answer is correct because the dog says in the paragraph that he is as thin as a rail. The word *as* signals that two things are being compared in a simile.

4. The phrase *once bitten, twice shy* means that someone who

  Ⓐ is very shy should avoid getting bitten.

   This answer is not correct because there are no details in the fable to hint at this meaning of the phrase. Neither animal in the story is shy, nor is either bitten.

  ● faced danger in the past is more careful in the future.

   This answer is correct because the details in the fable suggest that after facing the possibility of becoming the wolf's meal by lying in an unsafe place, the dog later protects himself by lying out of reach on the barn roof.

  Ⓒ was bitten once becomes twice as shy.

   This answer is not correct because there are no details in the fable to hint at this meaning of the phrase. Neither animal in the story is bitten, nor is either shy.

  Ⓓ bites someone else is less shy than other people.

   This answer is not correct because there are no details in the fable to hint at this meaning of the phrase. Neither animal bites someone else or appears to be shy.

MORE TO KNOW	• Think about what is being compared in a simile or a metaphor. Ask yourself, "What do the two things have in common?" This will help you create pictures in your mind.
	• Look at the sentences near an idiom. You might find context clues to help you figure out its meaning.

Read this tall tale about a remarkable woman. Then answer the questions.

Sally Ann Thunder Ann Whirlwind Crockett

Long ago on the Tennessee frontier, there lived a woman named Sally Ann. She was married to Davy Crockett, who liked to call her his sweet little wife. Sally Ann, however, wasn't exactly sweet or little. She had a quick temper and looked daggers at anyone who upset her. Sally Ann stood as tall as a young tree and had arms as big as a woodcutter. She liked to wear a bearskin for a dress and a hornet's nest for a bonnet.

People said that Sally Ann was made of thunder with a dash of whirlwind thrown in for good measure. So, she became known as Sally Ann Thunder Ann Whirlwind Crockett. Sally Ann walked like an ox and ran like a fox. She could leap over the Grand Canyon with both eyes shut. Furthermore, she could blow out the moonlight, ride a panther bareback, sing a wolf to sleep, and jump over her own shadow. Sally Ann also had a big sense of humor. She could laugh the bark off a pine tree.

Sally Ann feared nothing. But she never bragged. And she never fought any person or creature without a good reason.

5. The phrase *looked daggers at* means
   - Ⓐ "pointed at silently."
   - Ⓑ "stared at curiously."
   - Ⓒ "glared at angrily."
   - Ⓓ "peeked at quickly."

6. The tall tale says that Sally Ann *ran like a fox*. This means that Sally Ann was
   - Ⓐ quick.
   - Ⓑ sly.
   - Ⓒ strong.
   - Ⓓ quiet.

7. Sally Ann's height is compared to that of
   - Ⓐ a woodcutter.
   - Ⓑ the Grand Canyon.
   - Ⓒ a bear.
   - Ⓓ a young tree.

8. In paragraph 2, what does *for good measure* mean?
   - Ⓐ "finding the correct measurement"
   - Ⓑ "in addition to a certain amount"
   - Ⓒ "a helpful measuring tool"
   - Ⓓ "a small amount"

Read this song about a hardworking cowboy. Then answer the questions.

The Cowboy Song

All day on the prairie
    in a saddle I ride,
Not even a dog, boys,
    to trot by my side.
My fire I must kindle
    with chips gathered round,
And boil my own coffee
    without being ground.
My bread lacking leaven
    I bake in a pot,
And I sleep on the ground
    for want of a cot.

I wash in a puddle
    and wipe on a sack,
I carry my wardrobe
    along on my back.
My ceiling's the sky,
    my carpet the grass,

My music the lowing
    of herds as they pass.
My books are the brooks,
    my sermons the stones,
My <u>parson's</u> a wolf
    on a pulpit of bones.

parson: a preacher

9. In the song, the sky is compared to the cowboy's
   Ⓐ ceiling.
   Ⓑ carpet.
   Ⓒ parson.
   Ⓓ fire.

10. Which two things are compared in the song?
   Ⓐ the cowboy's books and some stones
   Ⓑ the cowboy's cot and the grass
   Ⓒ the cowboy's wardrobe and a sack
   Ⓓ the cowboy's music and the lowing of herds

11. The words *my books are the brooks* mean that the cowboy
   Ⓐ got his books wet.
   Ⓑ soaks up written words as if they were water.
   Ⓒ studies the brooks as he would study books.
   Ⓓ reads by the water.

12. Which of these is a metaphor?
   Ⓐ I boil my own coffee without being ground.
   Ⓑ My bread lacking leaven I bake in a pot.
   Ⓒ I carry my wardrobe along on my back.
   Ⓓ My parson's a wolf on a pulpit of bones.

TEST TIPS

- A test question about interpreting figurative language may ask you about the meaning of a simile, a metaphor, or an idiom.
- A test question about interpreting figurative language may ask you about things that are compared in the reading passage.

Read this newspaper ad for a special service. Then answer questions about the ad. Choose the best answer for Numbers 13 and 14.

Too Busy? Call Busy Bees!

Is the clutter in your house driving you up a wall? Are you going bananas thinking about everything you need to do? Is never having enough time bugging you? If you're ready to throw in the towel, let Busy Bee do it for you. We'll do your laundry and lots more, too.

There's no job Busy Bees won't do. We clean homes and offices inside and out. We walk dogs and feed fish. We buy groceries and cook meals. We wash cars and water lawns. We return purchases and library books. We even help kids with their homework.

Other businesses can't hold a candle to Busy Bees. Our workers are as quick as lightning and as quiet as mice.

Don't be afraid to admit you need help. Come clean, and call Busy Bees today. We'll go all out to help you.

13. In the ad, the workers' quickness is compared to
Ⓐ books.
Ⓑ mice.
Ⓒ lightning.
Ⓓ bees.

14. The phrase *can't hold a candle to* means
Ⓐ "are not careful about causing fires."
Ⓑ "are not as good as."
Ⓒ "are not quick as lightning."
Ⓓ "are not as bright as."

Read this tall tale. Then answer questions about the tall tale. Choose the best answer for Numbers 15 and 16.

The Popcorn Patch

"I had an old mule once upon a time that fooled himself clean to death," said Hank Huggins. "It happened down in Cade's Cove where I had planted me a little patch of corn, the kind that's used for popping. It was a hot day. I didn't want to go out plowing that morning, but my wife got after me. . . . Once my wife has set her mind to something, there's no peace until it's done. So I went out, hitched up the mule, and set off to plow the cornfield.

"Heavens to Betsy, it was hot in that cove! The mountains standing up all around kept out every breath of breeze. The place held the heat like an oven. July flies were a-droning in the trees, and the leaves hung as limp as a dog's tongue. It would be hard to say which was hotter, me or that old mule. Up and down the rows we went, a-toiling and a-sweating.

"Along towards noon it was broiling for certain. Even the old logs and stumps began to crawl off into the shade. Suddenly, I heard a crackling sound in the air. Before I could figure out what was happening, white flakes were a-flying all around. At first, I thought it was a snowstorm. Then I realized what it was: The blazing sun had set that corn a-popping, and it was falling like a snowstorm.

"That old mule of mine, he stopped and looked around. Then he began to shiver. He thought for sure he'd been overtaken by a howling blizzard. He stood there and squinched himself all up, like critters do when it's real cold.

" 'Get along there!' I hollered at him. 'It's nothing but popcorn!'

"But the poor thing couldn't understand. He'd never seen any popcorn before, and he thought it was snow. He just stood there, shaking and shivering in every limb. I couldn't do a thing with him. It was a crying shame. Before I could get that critter unhooked from the plow and out of there, he gave right up. He lay down in the row and froze to death— all covered up with popcorn."

15. The phrase *set her mind to something* means that Hank's wife

Ⓐ never stops thinking.

Ⓑ becomes determined.

Ⓒ likes to nag.

Ⓓ asks others for favors.

16. In the tall tale, the falling popcorn is compared to

Ⓐ cornstalks.

Ⓑ a mountain.

Ⓒ a snowstorm.

Ⓓ a dog's tongue.

What Is Summarizing?

A summary is a short statement that tells the main points or important ideas of something you have read or watched, such as a book or a movie. When you restate the important ideas, you are summarizing.

1 Write the name of a movie or TV show that you watched in the past few weeks.

_____

2 Write three of the important events from the movie or TV show.

_____

_____

_____

3 Write one sentence that tells how you would answer someone who asked you what the movie or TV show was mostly about. Include information about the important events in your sentence.

_____

_____

_____

 Work with a Partner

- Take turns summarizing books, movies, or TV shows.
- Make sure to tell about the most important ideas in one sentence.

- Identify a conclusion that summarizes the main idea (**GPI.R.1**)

How Do You Know What Makes a Good Summary?

A good summary of a reading passage depends on the kind of passage you are reading. If you are reading fiction, usually you will read about a character who has a problem. Your summary should tell about the character, the problem, and the solution. If you are reading nonfiction, your summary should tell about the main idea of the passage as well as the main points contained in the paragraphs.

Read this passage about Native American sign language. Think about what would make a good summary.

> Long ago, Native Americans developed a system of sign language. All tribes understood these signs. The signs were a helpful way to understand each other since not all tribes shared the same spoken language.
>
> Many Native Americans today still use the ancient form of sign language. Though it is no longer needed, it is an important link to their past.

1. Let's narrow down the main idea and the important points in this nonfiction passage.

   Look at the chart below. It shows the main idea and three important points about the main idea.

2. Use the main idea and important points to finish the one-sentence summary of the passage in the box at the bottom.

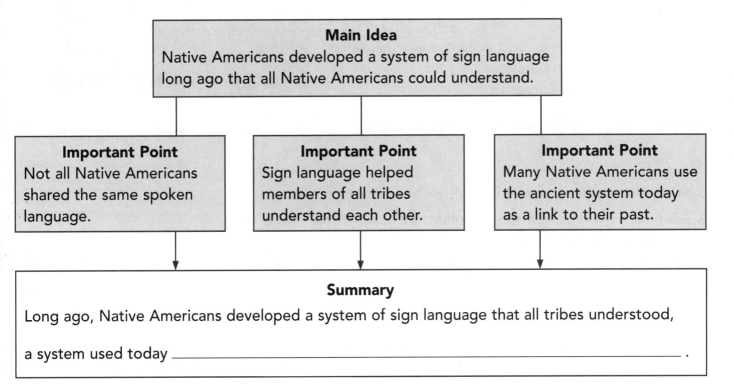

Main Idea
Native Americans developed a system of sign language long ago that all Native Americans could understand.

Important Point
Not all Native Americans shared the same spoken language.

Important Point
Sign language helped members of all tribes understand each other.

Important Point
Many Native Americans use the ancient system today as a link to their past.

Summary
Long ago, Native Americans developed a system of sign language that all tribes understood,

a system used today _____ .

WHAT TO KNOW

A summary is a short statement that tells the main points or important ideas of a reading passage. When you retell the important ideas in one sentence, you are **summarizing**.

- A summary is not stated in a reading passage. To create a summary, you must think about and retell the most important ideas.
- A good summary of fiction tells about the main character, the problem, and the solution.
- A good summary of nonfiction tells about the main idea of the passage, as well as the main ideas contained in the paragraphs.

Read this article about spiders. As you read, think about the most important ideas in the article. Then think about what you might tell someone who asks what the article is about.

Spiders spin webs that are sticky. They do this so that flies and other insects will become trapped in the web. Once a fly is trapped on the sticky threads, it cannot break free. But how do spiders walk on their own webs without getting trapped?

Spiders make several kinds of silk to build a web. One kind of silk is the sticky kind. Spiders use the sticky silk to catch insects. Another kind of silk is not sticky. Spiders use this silk to make the strong supporting threads of the web. Spiders know to walk only on the threads that aren't sticky.

The most important ideas in the article are:

Spiders do not get trapped in their webs, but insects do.

Spiders use two kinds of silk to build their webs—one kind is sticky, the other is not.

Spiders know not to walk on the sticky threads of their webs.

Here is what you might tell someone who asks what the article is about:

Insects get trapped on the sticky threads of spiders' webs, but spiders do not get trapped in their webs because they know to walk on the threads that aren't sticky.

Read this story about a girl named Keiko. As you read, think about the main character's problem and its solution. Then answer the questions.

Monster of the Deep

Keiko was lying in bed. She had just finished reading in her encyclopedia about the giant squid. This fierce creature exists way down deep in the dark, cold sea. The giant squid grows up to 70 feet long and weighs hundreds of pounds. Its eyes are the size of dinner plates. It has ten arms and a beak like a parrot. Sightings of giant squid are extremely rare. Giant squid are not found in the parts of the ocean where people often swim or go boating. Keiko shuddered at the thought of meeting one. Keiko was still thinking about the giant squid when she drifted off to sleep.

Keiko found herself in a boat enjoying a day on the ocean when a giant tentacle, or arm, reached overboard. The tentacle was covered with rows of suckers. Keiko had read that the suckers hold the squid's food as the tentacles carry it to the mouth. She didn't want to be a meal for a giant squid. Keiko screamed and moved away from the giant arm, but it kept moving and calling out her name. Keiko woke up shaking and sweating and saw her mom standing next to the bed. "What a nightmare! That's the last time I read about a scary animal before I go to sleep!"

1. What is Keiko's main problem in the story?
   - Ⓐ She was almost eaten by a giant squid.
   - Ⓑ She woke up in the middle of the night.
   - Ⓒ She had a nightmare after reading about a scary animal.
   - Ⓓ She could not go back to sleep after having a nightmare.

2. What is the best summary of the story?
   - Ⓐ A girl goes to bed after reading a book about a scary animal.
   - Ⓑ A girl was enjoying a day on the ocean when a giant squid reached overboard and frightened her.
   - Ⓒ After a girl has a nightmare, she decides never to read a scary book before going to bed.
   - Ⓓ A girl falls asleep while reading a book and then wakes up in the middle of the night.

Work with a Partner

- Talk about your answers to the questions.
- Tell why you chose your answers.
- Then talk about what you have learned so far about summarizing.

REVIEW	A summary is a short statement that tells the main points or important ideas of a reading passage. • A good summary of fiction tells about the main character's problem and its solution. • A good summary of nonfiction includes the main ideas of the selection.

Read this newspaper article about a new park. As you read, ask yourself, "What does a good summary of nonfiction include?" Then answer the questions.

Crane Park Officially Opens

By Jules Reed

Crane Park opened today to a huge crowd of excited children and adults. This new park is located in the southern part of town, near Turtle Pond.

Mayor Sims was on hand to help dedicate the park. Crane Park honors Michael Crane, a young ballplayer who has a rare bone disease. Michael can no longer play baseball. He does, however, spend lots of time with children and young adults.

Michael talks about ways to meet life's problems. Although he is only fifteen years old, Michael inspires people of all ages.

Crane Park has something for everyone. There are three ballparks, a track, and a playground. There is also a swimming area. Refreshment stands, picnic areas, and kayaks are all available for rent.

3. What is the main idea of the article?
   Ⓐ A new park opens to honor a young baseball player.
   Ⓑ A park has something for everyone.
   Ⓒ A young baseball player has a rare bone disease.
   Ⓓ A mayor helps dedicate a new park.

4. What is the best summary of the article?
   Ⓐ A young boy can no longer play baseball because of a rare bone disease.
   Ⓑ A new park honors a young boy with a rare bone disease who is an inspiration to many.
   Ⓒ A mayor helps dedicate a park to a young ballplayer.
   Ⓓ Many people are excited about the opening of a new park.

Which Answer Is Correct and Why?

Look at the answer choices for each question.
Read why each answer choice is correct or not correct.

3. **What is the main idea of the article?**

⬤ **A new park opens to honor a young baseball player.**

This answer is correct because it tells what the article is mostly about. Most of the facts and details in the article support this main idea.

Ⓑ **A park has something for everyone.**

This answer is not correct because it does not tell what the article is mostly about. This answer tells only about one detail that supports the main idea.

Ⓒ **A young baseball player has a rare bone disease.**

This answer is not correct because it does not tell what the article is mostly about. This answer tells only a detail that supports the main idea.

Ⓓ **A mayor helps dedicate a new park.**

This answer is not correct because it does not tell what the whole article is mostly about. This answer tells one detail that supports the main idea.

4. **What is the best summary of the article?**

Ⓐ **A young boy can no longer play baseball because of a rare bone disease.**

This answer is not correct because it states only one important detail from the article. A good summary of nonfiction includes the main ideas of the passage.

⬤ **A new park honors a young boy with a rare bone disease who is an inspiration to many.**

This answer is correct because it includes the most important ideas in the article. This answer summarizes the main points of what the article is about.

Ⓒ **A mayor helps dedicate a park to a young ballplayer.**

This answer is not correct because it does not tell enough about the most important ideas in the article, as a good summary of nonfiction should.

Ⓓ **Many people are excited about the opening of a new park.**

This answer is not correct because it tells only about one detail from the article. A good summary of nonfiction should include the main ideas of the whole passage.

MORE TO KNOW	• A good summary of fiction often tells about the theme, or message, of the story. • A good summary of nonfiction answers *who, what, when, where, why,* and *how* questions.

Read this article about the railroad. Then answer the questions.

In the 1500s, wagons were often pushed or pulled on wooden rails. The rails guided the wheels of the wagons. Horses had to pull, or men had to push, the wagons along the rails. Wagons such as these were used to carry ore from mines. These early rail systems were called wagon-ways. They didn't go far. They were also private. The public could not use them.

In 1803, the first public wagon-way opened in England. The wagons on it carried only goods. In 1807, the first wagon-way for passengers opened. People paid money to ride on the wagons that were pulled by horses.

A new invention soon brought changes. The first steam locomotive was built in Britain in 1804. It ran on the rails of wagon-ways. It was used to haul freight at coal mines and ironworks. The early locomotive had few uses. However, better locomotives were always being invented. Better rails were, too.

In 1825, a steam railway opened in England. It carried both freight and people. The first railroad across western North America was completed in 1869. It helped open the American West to settlers. By 1900, rail systems had spread throughout the world, and the railroad was born.

5. What is the article mostly about?
   - Ⓐ early wagon-ways
   - Ⓑ the history of the railroad
   - Ⓒ the first steam locomotives
   - Ⓓ the mining of ore and coal

6. What happened in 1825?
   - Ⓐ The first steam locomotive was built.
   - Ⓑ The first wagon-way for passengers opened.
   - Ⓒ Rail systems had spread throughout the world.
   - Ⓓ A new steam railway opened in England.

7. Early rail systems were called
   - Ⓐ railroads.
   - Ⓑ locomotives.
   - Ⓒ wagon-ways.
   - Ⓓ wagons.

8. What is a good summary of the article?
   - Ⓐ Horses no longer had to push or pull wagons after the steam locomotive was invented.
   - Ⓑ Steam locomotives had few uses until the 1800s.
   - Ⓒ Wagon-ways and steam locomotives led to the development of the railroad.
   - Ⓓ The history of the railroad can be traced back to the 1500s.

Read this story about two sisters. Then answer the questions.

Julia didn't want to go home. She couldn't face her sister, Anna. Julia had borrowed Anna's favorite blouse without asking. Now it was ruined.

When Julia got home, she tried to hide from Anna as long as possible. But when Anna came into Julia's bedroom to borrow a pencil, Julia could hide no longer. She swallowed hard and blurted out the truth without taking a breath.

"I ruined your favorite blouse at school today. Jason Holbrook spilled ketchup on me at lunch. Lydia tried to help me get it out, but we only made the stain worse. Please forgive me," Julia begged.

Anna didn't say a word. She just listened to her younger sister.

Julia continued. "I'm sorry. I shouldn't have borrowed your blouse without asking. But I'm going to make it up to you. I'll use my baby-sitting money to buy you a new blouse, any one you want."

"I wish you hadn't borrowed something of mine without asking," said Anna. "But at least you told me the truth." Anna then smiled and said, "And I'll take you up on your offer to buy me a new blouse."

9. Who is the main character in the story?
   Ⓐ Julia
   Ⓑ Jason
   Ⓒ Anna
   Ⓓ Lydia

10. What is the main problem in the story?
   Ⓐ A girl hides a favorite blouse from her sister.
   Ⓑ A girl does not want to go home.
   Ⓒ A girl is unhappy with her younger sister.
   Ⓓ A girl ruins her sister's favorite blouse.

11. How did Julia first try to solve her problem?
   Ⓐ by telling her sister she was sorry
   Ⓑ by hiding from her sister
   Ⓒ by trying to get the stain out of her sister's blouse
   Ⓓ by offering to buy her sister a new blouse

12. Which of these is a good summary of the story?
   Ⓐ A girl is afraid to tell her sister the truth about what happened at school.
   Ⓑ A girl ruins her sister's blouse, but offers to make it up by buying her a new one.
   Ⓒ A girl borrows her sister's favorite blouse without asking permission.
   Ⓓ A girl tries to hide the fact that she ruined her sister's favorite blouse.

TEST TIPS

- A test question about summarizing may ask you to choose the best summary of a reading passage. When you answer questions about summarizing, first determine if the reading passage is fiction or nonfiction. Then think about what is included in a good summary of fiction or of nonfiction.

- The answer to a test question about summarizing will not be directly stated in the reading passage. You must think about the most important ideas to find the best summary.

Read this fable about Wind and Thunder. Then answer questions about the fable. Choose the best answer for Numbers 13 and 14.

The Quarrel Between Wind and Thunder

Wind believed that he worked harder than anyone else. "I am the one who keeps the earth in good order. I do all of the work."

Thunder heard this and was instantly upset. "No you don't," said Thunder. "I keep the earth in good order. I do all of the work." Thunder didn't want anything more to do with Wind. So he went far away.

"I don't need you," called Wind. "I do all of the work anyway. I keep the earth in good order. I make the plants grow."

Wind wanted to show how powerful he was. He began to blow and blow, and then he blew some more. He kept blowing, but no plants grew. The earth slowly turned brown. The soil was parched, and everything was drying up.

Wind now knew that what he had said was not true. So he went to Thunder. "I cannot do all the work by myself. The earth needs us both."

Thunder came back. He let out a rumble, and then another and another. Soon rain began to fall to the earth. The earth slowly turned green once again. Wind tagged along behind Thunder, happy to blow among the tall grasses again. This is how Wind and Thunder came to work together to take care of the earth.

13. What is the main problem in the folktale?

Ⓐ Wind does not work as hard as Thunder.

Ⓑ Wind thinks he keeps the earth in good order all by himself.

Ⓒ Thunder doesn't want anything more to do with Wind.

Ⓓ The earth turns brown and everything dries up.

14. What is a good summary of the folktale?

Ⓐ Wind realizes that Thunder does all of the work after all.

Ⓑ Wind and Thunder have an argument that is never settled.

Ⓒ Wind learns that he needs Thunder to keep the earth in good order.

Ⓓ Wind learns that Thunder is more powerful than he is.

Read this tall tale about a sailor. Then answer questions about the tall tale. Choose the best answer for Numbers 15 and 16.

Old Stormalong

Alfred Bulltop Stormalong was famous for his big ways. By age 12, he stood 36 feet tall and had the hunger of 600 men. He ate ostrich eggs for breakfast and drank gallons of soup for lunch. For dinner, he'd eat enough shark to fill a warehouse.

Stormalong was too big to fit in any buildings in his town. So he chose the ocean as his home. "The sailor's life is the only one for me," said he.

Stormalong went to Boston Harbor and climbed aboard the *Lady of the Sea.* It was the biggest clipper ship in the Atlantic Ocean. He spent several years sailing the high seas on the sleek, wind-driven vessel. But he was never truly happy. Every night, he had to sleep in a rowboat by himself. The hammocks on the *Lady* were too small for the giant.

In good time, a ship was finally built that was just right for Stormalong. The *Courser* was the biggest clipper ship in the world. Her sails were so tall that they could touch the sun and the moon. It took 32 seamen just to pilot the wheel. Stormalong, though, could turn the wheel with just his pinkie.

One day, a fierce hurricane pushed the *Courser* toward some islands in the Caribbean Sea. Stormalong steered the ship clear of the islands, but then the storm grew fiercer. It drove the mighty *Courser* toward the Isthmus of Panama. The vessel ran right across the land, digging a deep ditch from the Atlantic Ocean on one side to the Pacific Ocean on the other side. That opening is now called the Panama Canal.

Stormalong lived to a ripe old age. Then one fine morning, Old Stormalong drew his last breath of ocean air and was gone. The men of the *Courser* buried the sailor by the shore. There he would always feel the salt spray of the sea.

15. What is the tall tale mostly about?
  Ⓐ a man who enjoys a life at sea
  Ⓑ a man who steers his ship through a hurricane
  Ⓒ a man who is so large that he chooses the sea as his home
  Ⓓ a man who drinks gallons of soup for lunch

16. Which of these is a good summary of the tall tale?
  Ⓐ A man accidentally creates the Panama Canal with his ship.
  Ⓑ A giant man spends a life of adventure at sea, the only place big enough for him.
  Ⓒ A man who stands 36 feet tall cannot fit in any buildings in his town.
  Ⓓ A man who dies at sea is buried by the shore so he'll always feel the spray of the sea.

Read this folktale from Africa. Then answer questions about the folktale. Choose the best answer for Numbers 1 through 6.

The Tug of War

Hare had always been a lazy creature. Even when he got married, he was lazy. Go work in the fields so that he and his wife could eat? Not on your life. Though Hare was lazy, he often was very clever. He soon thought up a way to get all of his work done without having to lift a finger himself.

Hare found a long rope and went to search for Hippo. Hippo was standing in a pool of mud at the edge of a field.

"Let's play a game, Hippo. Let me tie this rope around you and see if I can pull you out of the mud and into the middle of the field."

"You can try," said Hippo, "but I don't think you'll be able to do it."

So Hare tied the rope around Hippo nice and tight. "I'm going to go into the field," said Hare, "and pull on the other end of the rope. When you see the rope move, pull like mad."

"Okay," said Hippo. He knew he was stronger than Hare. He also knew that if he pulled on the rope, he would pull Hare right into the mud with him.

Hare then went across the field to look for Elephant in the woods. He asked Elephant if he wanted to play the same game. "Will you let me tie this rope around you?"

Elephant agreed, knowing that he was stronger than Hare. As Hare left, he told Elephant to start pulling when he saw the rope move.

Hare gave a tug on the middle of the rope, where neither Hippo nor Elephant could see him. Right away, Hippo and Elephant began pulling on the rope. They pulled and pulled. First Hippo was pulled onto the edge of the field. Then Elephant was. They pulled each other back and forth all day and night. They pulled until the sun went down the next day. Finally, they both fell down exhausted, wondering how Hare had won.

At the same time, Hare was out in his fields. He was pleased to see that the ground was all dug up and ready for planting. Hare smiled. "And I didn't have to do any digging or plowing myself."

Identifying Author's Purpose

1. The author wrote this folktale mainly to
   - Ⓐ entertain readers with a story about a lazy, but clever, hare.
   - Ⓑ persuade readers to feel sorry for Elephant and Hippo.
   - Ⓒ inform readers about farming in Africa.
   - Ⓓ describe how to play the game of tug of war.

Identifying Author's Purpose

2. You know your answer to question 1 is correct because the folktale mainly
   - Ⓐ contains many details that describe something.
   - Ⓑ provides facts or tells readers how to do something.
   - Ⓒ tries to convince readers of something.
   - Ⓓ tells a story that is enjoyable to read.

Interpreting Figurative Language

3. In the first paragraph, the phrase *not on your life* means
   - Ⓐ "not unless it causes your death."
   - Ⓑ "not if you put my life in danger."
   - Ⓒ "not for any reason, no matter what."
   - Ⓓ "not while you are still living."

Interpreting Figurative Language

4. In paragraph 5, what does the phrase *pull like mad* mean?
   - Ⓐ "pull as if you are mad"
   - Ⓑ "pull with an angry look on your face"
   - Ⓒ "pull like a crazed animal"
   - Ⓓ "pull as hard as you can"

Summarizing

5. What is the main problem in the story?
   - Ⓐ Animals must get their fields ready for planting.
   - Ⓑ Hippo cannot figure out how he lost a game of tug of war.
   - Ⓒ Elephant and Hippo are not as strong as they thought they were.
   - Ⓓ Hare does not want to work in his fields so he and his wife can eat.

Summarizing

6. What is the best summary of the folktale?
   - Ⓐ Hare challenges Hippo and Elephant to a game of tug of war.
   - Ⓑ Hare comes up with a clever trick to get others to do his work for him.
   - Ⓒ Hare wins a game of tug of war with Hippo and Elephant.
   - Ⓓ Hare and his friends work in the fields to get them ready for planting.

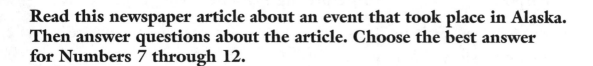

Read this newspaper article about an event that took place in Alaska. Then answer questions about the article. Choose the best answer for Numbers 7 through 12.

The Arctic News   January 28, 1925

The people of Nome, Alaska, were in trouble. An illness called diphtheria was sweeping through the town. People were dying, and many more might die soon. They needed medicine badly, but the nearest supply was hundreds of miles to the south in Anchorage. Winter storms raged. No planes could fly. Snow buried the railroad tracks. How could the medicine get from Anchorage to Nome?

By dogsled—that was the only way. Teams of dogs took turns traveling north like runners in a relay race.

The first team set out pulling their sled loaded with the medicine. They traveled many miles and then met up with the second team. The second team took over until it met up with the third team. So it went until an exhausted dog team pulled into a little town just 60 miles south of Nome. The snowstorm was getting wilder by the minute. The temperature was 30 below zero and falling. The man driving the sled couldn't see the nose in front of his face.

The driver of the fresh team was a man named Gunnar Kaasen. He decided to take a chance and head out into the deadly storm. He put his smartest dog, Balto, in the lead. Part wolf, Balto was the most dependable dog Kaasen had ever known. Kaasen would not be able to see well enough to steer the sled. He would have to let Balto lead the way.

The trail disappeared under whirling snow. Balto pushed on. The team hauled across sea ice that rumbled and buckled. Balto pushed on. When the ice boomed like thunder and cracked wide open, Balto led the team miles around the water. Hour after hour, Balto pushed on through the freezing storm, through snowdrifts that almost buried them all. He did not let the dogs rest, for resting might mean freezing to death.

At last, Balto led the dogs, Kaasen, and the valuable medicine into Nome. Their journey had taken an unbelievable 20 hours.

Identifying Author's Purpose

7. The author's main purpose in the first paragraph is to
   Ⓐ describe a situation in Nome, Alaska, one winter.
   Ⓑ persuade readers that diphtheria is a deadly disease.
   Ⓒ explain why Nome is often hit hard by storms.
   Ⓓ delight readers with a story about an amazing dog.

Identifying Author's Purpose

8. Paragraph 5 mainly tells
   Ⓐ a funny story about a stubborn dog.
   Ⓑ how the dogsled teams took turns traveling north.
   Ⓒ about Balto's bravery.
   Ⓓ why readers should believe that Balto would become famous.

Interpreting Figurative Language

9. In paragraph 2, the writer compares the dog teams to
   Ⓐ a pack of wolves.
   Ⓑ runners in a relay race.
   Ⓒ winter storms.
   Ⓓ fast planes.

Interpreting Figurative Language

10. Which of these is a simile?
    Ⓐ most dependable dog
    Ⓑ sweeping through the town
    Ⓒ cracked wide open
    Ⓓ boomed like thunder

Summarizing

11. What is the article mostly about?
    Ⓐ a terrible illness called diphtheria
    Ⓑ a dependable dog that is part wolf
    Ⓒ teams of dogs that must carry medicine through a horrible storm
    Ⓓ a sled driver who must put together a brave team of dogs

Summarizing

12. What is a good summary for the article?
    Ⓐ People in Nome, Alaska, are in danger of dying from diphtheria.
    Ⓑ Dangerous weather conditions make it almost impossible for sled dogs to travel.
    Ⓒ A sled driver puts his smartest dog in the lead of a team of sled dogs.
    Ⓓ Sled dogs guide their driver through blinding snow to deliver important medicine.

Read this tall tale about an African American folk hero. Then answer questions about the tall tale. Choose the best answer for Numbers 1 through 12.

When John Henry was born, he was the most powerful-looking infant anyone had ever seen. He had broad shoulders, and arms as thick as stovepipes. His smile was so bright that it lit up the dark sky.

The mighty child grew faster than a weed. By the time he was ten, he was hammering steel for the railroad. From dawn to dusk, he pounded steel spikes into solid rock with a long-handled hammer, making deep holes. Workers then filled the holes with explosives and blasted the rock away to make tunnels.

By his twenties, John Henry was the best "steel-drivin' man" in the country. His hammer moved as quick as lightning. He always kept a pail of water nearby to cool the hammer down. Most of the railroad bosses wanted John Henry to work for them. But one boss convinced John Henry to lead the team of steel drivers on the Big Bend Tunnel being built in the Allegheny Mountains of West Virginia.

One day, a fast-talking salesman brought a steam drill to the work site. He boasted that the steam drill could dig holes faster than a dozen men. John Henry looked at that steam drill and thought of all the workers who would lose their jobs to machines. Then he called out, "Well, a man ain't nothin' but a man. But a man's just got to do his best. And before I let a steam drill beat me down, I'd rather die with a hammer in my hand."

So, John Henry entered a race to prove that he could drive a hammer faster than any machine. As he tunneled into the mountain, he hammered faster and faster and harder and harder. His hammer glowed white-hot, like a burning coal. As he dug deeper and deeper into the tunnel, the crowd outside could still hear that cold steel ring.

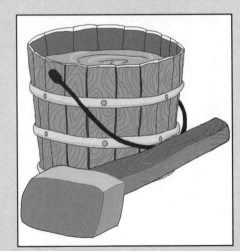

When the race was over, John Henry had driven two 7-foot holes into the rock. The steam drill had made only a 9-foot shaft. John Henry beat the steam drill, but he had hammered so hard that his great heart burst. And he laid down his hammer and died.

Finding Main Idea

1. What is the tall tale mostly about?
   - (A) life as a worker on the railroad
   - (B) the worries of a steel driver
   - (C) a strong man who died doing his best
   - (D) a machine that could work faster than all men

Recognizing Cause and Effect

4. Because his hammer moved so fast,
   - (A) John Henry was always racing against the other steel drivers.
   - (B) John Henry always kept a pail of water nearby to cool it down.
   - (C) John Henry developed broad shoulders and thick arms.
   - (D) John Henry was challenged to a race against a steam drill.

Recalling Facts and Details

2. John Henry began working for the railroad when he was
   - (A) an infant.
   - (B) ten years old.
   - (C) seven years old.
   - (D) in his twenties.

Comparing and Contrasting

5. How was John Henry different from the other steel drivers?
   - (A) He was the only one hired to work on the Big Bend Tunnel.
   - (B) He was the only one who could tunnel into a mountain.
   - (C) He hammered steel into rock, but they only used explosives.
   - (D) He was faster and more powerful than they were.

Understanding Sequence

3. The boxes tell about some things in the story.

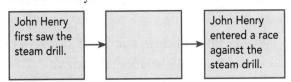

| John Henry first saw the steam drill. | → | | → | John Henry entered a race against the steam drill. |

What belongs in the empty box?
   - (A) John Henry accepted a job working on the Big Bend Tunnel.
   - (B) John Henry's great heart burst.
   - (C) John Henry thought of all the workers who would lose their jobs.
   - (D) John Henry was the best "steel-drivin' man" in the country.

Making Predictions

6. Predict what might have happened if John Henry had lived longer.
   - (A) He would have become too proud.
   - (B) He would have gotten tired of his job.
   - (C) He would have continued to work hard.
   - (D) He would have been replaced by a machine.

Finding Word Meaning in Context

7. In the last paragraph, you can tell that a *shaft* is
   - Ⓐ an arrow or a spear.
   - Ⓑ a ray or a beam.
   - Ⓒ a deep, narrow passage.
   - Ⓓ a tall, rounded hill.

Identifying Author's Purpose

10. The story was probably written in order to
    - Ⓐ describe steam drills.
    - Ⓑ explain how railroad tunnels are made.
    - Ⓒ persuade readers to support workers' rights.
    - Ⓓ entertain readers with a story about a folk hero.

Drawing Conclusions and Making Inferences

8. You can tell that John Henry
   - Ⓐ was not very sure of himself.
   - Ⓑ acted without thinking.
   - Ⓒ was in poor health.
   - Ⓓ was brave and determined.

Interpreting Figurative Language

11. The words *as quick as lightning* mean that John Henry's hammer
    - Ⓐ made deep holes.
    - Ⓑ moved incredibly fast.
    - Ⓒ was too hot to hold.
    - Ⓓ was stronger than metal.

Distinguishing Between Fact and Opinion

9. Which of these is an *opinion* about John Henry?
   - Ⓐ He was the most powerful-looking infant anyone had ever seen.
   - Ⓑ Most of the railroad bosses wanted him to work for them.
   - Ⓒ He could drive a hammer faster than a steam drill.
   - Ⓓ He swung a hammer hard and fast.

Summarizing

12. Which of these is the best summary of the tall tale?
    - Ⓐ A fast-talking salesman boasts about the job a steam drill can do.
    - Ⓑ A man tries to show that a man can be just as good as a machine.
    - Ⓒ A man leads a team of steel drivers to work on tunnels in West Virginia.
    - Ⓓ A race kills a man who was trying to show that he was the best steel driver in the country.

Read this article about the history of numbers. Then answer questions about the article. Choose the best answer for Numbers 13 through 24.

The early Egyptians invented one of the first number systems about 5,000 years ago. They based their system on the number 10. They most likely did this because it equaled the number of fingers on both hands. The Egyptians used symbols to stand for numbers. Each symbol stood for a specific value. For example, ∩ meant 10, ∩∩ meant 20, and so on. Egyptian numbers could be written and read from right to left, left to right, or up and down. The order of the symbols did not matter.

The ancient Chinese also developed a number system based on 10. They showed their numbers using small sticks. Where the sticks were put told a number's value. For example, ┰≡╥ was 637, but ╥≡┰ was 736.

The ancient Romans chose letters to stand for numbers. They based their number system on 5. The letters I, II, and III stood for 1, 2, and 3. The letters V, X, L, C, D, and M stood for 5, 10, 50, 100, 500, and 1,000. The letters were read in order from left to right. The values of the letters were either added or subtracted. When a letter that had the same value or smaller came after another letter, their values were added. For example, VI

This sign shows the number 89.

was 5 + 1, or 6, and XX was 10 + 10, or 20. When a letter with a smaller value came right before a letter with a larger value, the lower value was subtracted from the higher one. So, IV was 5 – 1, or 4, and XL was 50 – 10, or 40.

The Hindus of India figured out that they could use just 9 symbols to represent all numbers. They used the numbers 1 through 9. The placement of each symbol set its value. This made it possible to write a huge number, such as 895,673,421, without taking up a lot of space. The Hindus also invented the symbol 0. Its placement makes a difference in the value of a number. The Hindus taught their 10 numerals to Arab traders, who then used them in Europe. When the Europeans came to America in the 1600s, they brought the Arabic numerals with them. These are the numerals we use today.

Finding Main Idea

13. The best title for this article is
    (A) "Letters for Numbers."
    (B) "Why Zero Was Invented."
    (C) "The First Number System."
    (D) "The History of Numbers."

Recalling Facts and Details

14. Who invented Arabic numerals?
    (A) Arabs
    (B) Hindus
    (C) Europeans
    (D) Americans

Understanding Sequence

15. Which type of number system came last?
    (A) one in which the order of the symbols did not matter
    (B) one that used the symbol 0 to show place value
    (C) one that used stick arrangements to tell a value
    (D) one based on the number 5

Recognizing Cause and Effect

16. The Egyptians most likely based their number system on 10 because
    (A) it equaled the number of a person's fingers and toes.
    (B) they didn't know about the Roman number system.
    (C) it equaled the number of fingers on both hands.
    (D) it was easy to show the number 10 with sticks.

Comparing and Contrasting

17. How were the Egyptian and the Chinese number systems alike?
    (A) Both were based on the number 10.
    (B) Both showed numbers with sticks.
    (C) Numbers in both systems were read only from left to right.
    (D) Letters stood for numbers in both systems.

Making Predictions

18. Predict how life would be different today if there were no numbers.
    (A) People would not be able to farm, fish, or hunt.
    (B) People would not be able to communicate with each other.
    (C) People would have different ways of adding, measuring, and estimating.
    (D) People would have to depend more on the kindness of others.

Finding Word Meaning in Context

19. In the last paragraph, the best meaning of the word *represent* is

Ⓐ "to take up space."

Ⓑ "to invent something new."

Ⓒ "to speak or act for someone else."

Ⓓ "to stand for something."

Identifying Author's Purpose

22. What is the author's main purpose for writing the article?

Ⓐ to describe our present number system to readers

Ⓑ to explain different number systems to readers

Ⓒ to persuade readers to learn more about other number systems

Ⓓ to entertain readers with details about other cultures

Drawing Conclusions and Making Inferences

20. There is enough information in the article to show that

Ⓐ the Hindus' number system was less complicated than other systems.

Ⓑ Roman numerals are no longer used.

Ⓒ the Chinese sometimes ran out of sticks to show numbers.

Ⓓ letters are easier to draw than symbols.

Interpreting Figurative Language

23. In the last paragraph, what do the words *figured out* mean?

Ⓐ "drew a shape or design"

Ⓑ "solved a math problem"

Ⓒ "understood something"

Ⓓ "found out something's worth"

Distinguishing Between Fact and Opinion

21. Which of these is a *fact*?

Ⓐ The Egyptians weren't good at keeping numbers in order.

Ⓑ The Chinese stick arrangement was too complicated.

Ⓒ The Romans' number system was the best.

Ⓓ The Hindus used 9 symbols and 0 for larger numbers.

Summarizing

24. What is a good summary of the article?

Ⓐ Throughout history, different civilizations have invented different number systems.

Ⓑ The early Egyptians invented one of the first number systems about 5,000 years ago.

Ⓒ Hindus developed the number system used in the United States today.

Ⓓ Most number systems are based on 10 because that is the number of fingers on both hands.

**Read this book report about an important Native American woman.
Then answer questions about the book report. Choose the best answer
for Numbers 25 through 36.**

The biography *The Bird Woman* is about a remarkable Native American. Her name was Sacajawea. After reading this book, I feel as if I've gotten to know this brave woman.

The story begins with Sacajawea's birth. She was born some time around 1788. She lived among the Shoshone in what is now Idaho. When Sacajawea was only four years old, an enemy tribe captured her. Her kidnappers took her to the area that is now North Dakota. There, Sacajawea was sold to a French-Canadian trapper named Toussaint Charbonneau. He became her husband when Sacajawea was 16.

Sacajawea and Charbonneau were staying at Fort Mandan in North Dakota. There, they met Meriwether Lewis and William Clark in 1804. President Thomas Jefferson had hired Lewis and Clark to explore the Louisiana Territory. The United States had just bought this huge parcel of land from France. The Lewis and Clark expedition consisted of more than 40 men. They started their journey in St. Louis, Missouri. They hoped to find a water route across the Rocky Mountains to the Pacific Ocean.

Lewis and Clark asked Charbonneau to join their expedition as a guide. Sacajawea also wanted to see the "Big Waters," her name for the Pacific. She was the only woman to join the expedition. She carried her newborn baby boy on her back as they traveled. The explorers faced grizzly bears, steep cliffs, and fierce rapids. Sacajawea proved to be a valuable member of the group. She taught the men which plants could be used for medicine. She made buckskin clothes for them. She also helped them communicate with Native Americans they met along the way.

When Lewis and Clark reached the Rockies, they realized that they could not continue their journey by water. Things began to look up, though, when they met a group of Shoshone led by Sacajawea's long-lost brother. Sacajawea persuaded her brother to trade with the explorers for the horses they needed.

Sacajawea stayed with the expedition all the way to the Pacific Ocean and partway home. Sacajawea died when she was only 26. Her life was short, but her name lives on as an important woman in history.

Finding Main Idea

25. What is the book report mostly about?
- (A) famous explorers
- (B) the Louisiana Territory
- (C) a Native American heroine
- (D) the Lewis and Clark expedition

Recognizing Cause and Effect

28. Which of these is <u>not</u> a reason that Sacajawea was important to the expedition?
- (A) She helped the men communicate with Native Americans.
- (B) She had a baby boy with her.
- (C) She taught the men which plants could be used for medicine.
- (D) She made buckskin clothes for the men.

Recalling Facts and Details

26. Where did Sacajawea meet Lewis and Clark?
- (A) Idaho
- (B) Missouri
- (C) North Dakota
- (D) Louisiana

Comparing and Contrasting

29. What was one major difference between Sacajawea and the other explorers?
- (A) She was the only one who was married.
- (B) She was the only one who was a woman.
- (C) She was the only valuable member of the group.
- (D) She was the only one who knew the way across the Rockies.

Understanding Sequence

27. What happened immediately after Sacajawea was captured?
- (A) She married Toussaint Charbonneau.
- (B) She was sold to a French-Canadian trapper.
- (C) She met Lewis and Clark.
- (D) She was taken to the area that is now North Dakota.

Making Predictions

30. What might have happened if the expedition hadn't met the Shoshone?
- (A) The group would have starved to death.
- (B) The journey west would have been even more difficult.
- (C) Other Native Americans would have gladly helped the explorers.
- (D) Sacajawea would never have known that she was kidnapped as a child.

Finding Word Meaning in Context

31. In this book report, the best meaning for the word *expedition* is
    - (A) "a short trip to do something fun outside."
    - (B) "a special vacation out West."
    - (C) "a group making a long trip, usually for exploring."
    - (D) "quickness."

Identifying Author's Purpose

34. Paragraph 2 was written mainly to
    - (A) describe life in the early 1800s.
    - (B) encourage readers to read about famous Native Americans.
    - (C) entertain readers with tales about Lewis and Clark.
    - (D) inform readers about Sacajawea's early life.

Drawing Conclusions and Making Inferences

32. You can tell that the reviewer
    - (A) considers Sacajawea a hero.
    - (B) feels sorry for Sacajawea.
    - (C) is interested in the history of Native American people.
    - (D) believes the expedition was poorly planned.

Interpreting Figurative Language

35. In paragraph 5, the phrase *things began to look up* means that
    - (A) the expedition was nearing the top of the Rockies.
    - (B) the explorers had respect for the Shoshone.
    - (C) conditions were improving for the explorers.
    - (D) the explorers saw many birds flying overhead.

Distinguishing Between Fact and Opinion

33. Which of these expresses an *opinion* about Sacajawea?
    - (A) She had a short life.
    - (B) She was a famous Native American woman.
    - (C) She went on the journey shortly after giving birth.
    - (D) She was a remarkable Native American woman.

Summarizing

36. Which of these best summarizes the information in the article?
    - (A) Sacajawea accompanied Lewis and Clark on their exploration of the west.
    - (B) Explorers faced numerous dangers as they explored the Louisiana Territory.
    - (C) The Lewis and Clark expedition consisted of over 40 men, but only one woman.
    - (D) Sacajawea was an important member of the Lewis and Clark expedition.

Read this story about a boy who has just arrived in New York. Then answer questions about the story. Choose the best answer for Numbers 37 through 48.

Sanjeeve waited patiently at Grand Central Station in New York City. He was waiting for his host family to arrive. Sanjeeve would be attending school for one year in New York. He would miss his family. But he was excited about being in a new country, a new place.

Sanjeeve stood near the information booth of the train station, under a clock that had four faces. This was where he and his host family agreed to meet. It was a good plan. The train station was bustling with people and activity.

Sanjeeve and Jeremy Stein had exchanged e-mails over the summer. They were both the same age and in the same grade. Sanjeeve learned a lot about America, and Jeremy learned a lot about Sanjeeve's homeland of India. Even though they lived in different countries, the two boys had lots in common. Sanjeeve loved to explore new places, and Jeremy enjoyed meeting new people. Sanjeeve had told Jeremy all about the places he wanted to visit while he was in New York. There were many sights he wanted to see, but the Statue of Liberty topped his list. They also exchanged photographs of themselves and their families. Sanjeeve knew exactly what Jeremy looked like. He scanned the crowd like a hawk, searching for his friend and waiting for his new adventure to begin.

Finally Sanjeeve saw Jeremy. He was holding a small American flag that he gave to Sanjeeve. The boys greeted each other warmly and shook hands.

In the car, Jeremy explained the meaning of the flag. "Each star represents a state. The stripes are symbols for the thirteen original colonies. The flag is a symbol of freedom. The color red stands for courage. The white stands for liberty. The blue stands for loyalty."

Soon Sanjeeve and the Steins arrived at Battery Park. "Let's get started seeing all the sights," said Mrs. Stein. They all took the ferry across the harbor to visit the Statue of Liberty. Next they visited Ellis Island and the United Nations building. When the day ended, Sanjeeve sent an e-mail to his family. He wrote about all the details of his day and how much fun he had. He also told them how much he missed them already. Then Sanjeeve climbed into bed. He fell right to sleep, with a big smile on his face.

Finding Main Idea

37. What is the main idea of paragraph 1?
- Ⓐ A boy gets lost at a train station in New York City.
- Ⓑ A boy travels to New York City to see Grand Central Station.
- Ⓒ A boy enjoys spending time with his host family in New York.
- Ⓓ A boy waits at a train station for his host family to arrive.

Recalling Fact and Details

38. Sanjeeve is staying in New York for
- Ⓐ one week.
- Ⓑ one month.
- Ⓒ one year.
- Ⓓ an entire summer.

Understanding Sequence

39. The boxes tell about some of the things that happened in the story.

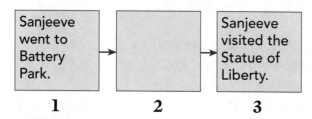

Sanjeeve went to Battery Park.		Sanjeeve visited the Statue of Liberty.
1	**2**	**3**

Which of these belongs in box 2?
- Ⓐ Sanjeeve visited the United Nations.
- Ⓑ Sanjeeve rode a ferry across the harbor.
- Ⓒ Sanjeeve learned about the American flag.
- Ⓓ Sanjeeve visited Ellis Island.

Recognizing Cause and Effect

40. Sanjeeve recognized Jeremy because
- Ⓐ he had seen a picture of Jeremy.
- Ⓑ he had spent time with him before.
- Ⓒ Jeremy had visited him in India over the summer.
- Ⓓ Jeremy described what he looked like.

Comparing and Contrasting

41. In the story, Sanjeeve is compared to a
- Ⓐ statue.
- Ⓑ clock.
- Ⓒ train.
- Ⓓ hawk.

Making Predictions

42. Which of these would Sanjeeve probably want to do tomorrow?
- Ⓐ play video games by himself
- Ⓑ shop for new clothes
- Ⓒ visit the Empire State Building
- Ⓓ see what his new school looks like

Finding Word Meaning in Context

43. The best meaning for *bustling* is
- Ⓐ "tiresome."
- Ⓑ "lively."
- Ⓒ "delightful."
- Ⓓ "gleaming."

Identifying Author's Purpose

46. The story was written mainly to
- Ⓐ get readers to visit other countries.
- Ⓑ entertain readers with an enjoyable story about a boy traveler.
- Ⓒ tell readers about sights to see in New York.
- Ⓓ describe what it is like to travel from India to New York.

Drawing Conclusions and Making Inferences

44. Which word best describes Sanjeeve?
- Ⓐ bashful
- Ⓑ obedient
- Ⓒ adventurous
- Ⓓ fearless

Interpreting Figurative Language

47. The words *topped his list* tell you that the Statue of Liberty
- Ⓐ was the only place Sanjeeve did not want to visit.
- Ⓑ was the only place Sanjeeve wanted to visit.
- Ⓒ was the tallest place Sanjeeve wanted to visit.
- Ⓓ was the place Sanjeeve most wanted to visit.

Distinguishing Between Fact and Opinion

45. Which statement tells a *fact*?
- Ⓐ Sanjeeve had the best day ever in New York.
- Ⓑ Mrs. Stein was a perfect tour guide.
- Ⓒ Jeremy should do everything he can to make Sanjeeve feel welcome.
- Ⓓ Sanjeeve will attend school in New York for one year.

Summarizing

48. What is a good summary for the story?
- Ⓐ A boy meets his host family for the first time.
- Ⓑ A boy enjoys learning about America and New York City.
- Ⓒ A boy arrives in New York City to begin a one-year adventure in a new country.
- Ⓓ A boy from India comes to America hoping to see some interesting places.